Live Action English
INTERACTIVE

WORKBOOK

Level 1
Low Beginning

Elizabeth Kuizenga Romijn

Command Performance Language Institute
1755 Hopkins Street
Berkeley, CA 94707
Tel/Fax: 510-524-1191
consee@aol.com
www.cpli.net

This workbook for use with the software
Live Action English Interactive
and a similar workbook for high beginning and low intermediate students
are published by the
Command Performance Language Institute,
which features
Total Physical Response products,
visually-oriented
materials for language teaching,
and other fine products
related to language acquisition
and teaching.

To obtain copies of the workbooks,
the software *Live Action English Interactive*
and the book *Live Action English*
contact one of the distributors listed on the final page.

Drawings by
Tamara Romijn &
Elizabeth Kuizenga Romijn

Photography by
Larry Statan
Miguel Díaz
Contee Seely &
Elizabeth Kuizenga Romijn

The software *Live Action English Interactive* was created by
Elizabeth Kuizenga Romijn
Contee Seely
Larry Statan
Elizabeth Hanson-Smith &
Robert Wachman

Map excerpt on page 49 from Oakland Berkeley Western Contra Costa map copyright
© by King of the Road & Thomas Bros. Maps.

First edition published March, 2005
Printed in Ecuador with pride at Imprenta Mariscal.
ISBN 0-929724-61-5

Note to the Student

The exercises in this workbook are only a small part of the Live Action English course. You will see a lot of English and action in the *Live Action English Interactive* computer program. And your teacher will show you many other activities in the classroom. Every day you will participate in some actions, and then you will practice talking about the actions with your teacher and classmates. It is important to attend class every day to hear your teacher speaking English, and to practice the verbs and other vocabulary with your classmates. Then the exercises in this workbook will be easy!

IMPORTANT
Note to the Teacher

Most of the exercises in this workbook require the use of the **Teacher's Resource Guide** which is available for FREE at www.cpli.net. It is important that you take the time and effort to download, read, and use the many TPR (Total Physical Response) activities and dictations presented in the Guide.

The written exercises in this workbook are very simple, and meant only as the last step of a much richer and more complex process of language acquisition. The classroom activities set out in the **Teacher's Resource Guide** will help your students to use the language of the action series actively and physically, thereby engaging both sides of the brain for a full and natural language learning/acquisition experience.

A unique feature of the guide is the use of *Recurrent Grammar*, students experiencing and using again and again the same grammatical features in a variety of contexts. This enables students to truly acquire these features.

In addition to these activities, there are word searches, word scrambles, and bingo games for each unit in the **Teacher's Resource Guide**.

SO DOWNLOAD IT, READ IT AND USE IT!
IT'S FREE!

CONTENTS

Teacher:
Be sure to
download the
FREE
Teacher's Resource Guide

It will help you to significantly improve and accelerate acquisition and learning by your students. See the note to the teacher on page *iii*.

UNIT 1   GOOD MORNING

 1. Wake up!

 2. Stretch and yawn and rub your eyes.

 3. Get up.

 4. Do your exercises.

 5. Wash your face.

 6. Get dressed.

 7. Make the bed.

 8. Eat breakfast.

 9. Read the newspaper.

 10. Brush your teeth.

 11. Put on your sweater.

 12. Kiss your family goodbye.

 13. Leave the house.

PRESENT PROGRESSIVE, LONG ANSWERS

Complete the answers with the correct possessive adjective:

his   her   their   our   your   my

1. What is she doing?

    She's washing _____ face.

2. What are you doing?

    I'm rubbing _____ eyes.

3. What are they doing?

    They're brushing _____ teeth.

4. What is he doing?

    He's putting on _____ sweater.

5. What are we doing?

    We're doing _____ exercises.

6. What am I doing?

    You're kissing _____ family goodbye.

Now practice with a classmate. Point to a photo and ask the question. Check the answer.

PRESENT PROGRESSIVE, SHORT ANSWERS

Look at the picture. Complete the Short Answer with the correct form of the verb TO BE:

is   isn't   are   aren't

1. Is she rubbing her eyes?   No, she _____ .

2. Is she getting dressed?   Yes, she _____ .

3. Are they reading the newspaper?   Yes, they _____ .

4. Are they brushing their teeth?   No, they _____ .

5. Is he leaving the house?   No, he _____ .

6. Is he stretching and yawning?   Yes, he _____ .

7. Are we eating breakfast?   No, we _____ .

8. Are we making the bed?   Yes, we _____ .

Now practice with a classmate.

PRESENT TENSE CONVERSATION

Complete the answers with personal information about your morning every day.

1. What time do you wake up in the morning?

    I wake up at _____ .

2. What time do you get up?

    I get up at _____ .

3. Do you stretch and yawn before or after you get up?

    I stretch and yawn _____ I get up.

4. Do you do your exercises?
    a. Yes, I do.
    b. No, I don't.

5. Who makes your bed?
    a. I make my bed.
    b. My _____ makes my bed.
    c. Nobody makes my bed.

6. Do you brush your teeth before or after breakfast?

    I brush my teeth _____ breakfast.

7. What do you eat for breakfast?

    I eat _____ for breakfast.

8. Do you read the newspaper in the morning?
    a. Yes, I do.
    b. No, I don't.

9. What time do you leave the house?

    I leave the house at _____ .

Every Morning

Every morning Carol wakes up at 7:00. She gets up and does her exercises. After that she washes her face. Then she gets dressed and makes her bed. She eats breakfast and reads the newspaper. Then she brushes her teeth. Carol puts on her sweater and kisses her family goodbye. She leaves the house at 8:30.

PERSONAL INFORMATION

wake up before 5:00 in the morning
get up after noon
do my exercises in the morning
wash my face in the morning
read the newspaper in the morning
read the newspaper in English
brush my teeth before breakfast
kiss my family in the morning
eat a big breakfast
get dressed before breakfast
make my bed
stretch and yawn before I get up

Complete the sentences with phrases from the list above, or other activities from the lesson.

I always _____

I never _____

Sometimes I _____

I usually _____

I often _____

I hardly ever _____

Now write a few more sentences about your morning using frequency adverbs:

_____

_____

_____

PAST TENSE

1. Who stretched and yawned? _____ did.

2. Who rubbed her eyes? _____ did.

3. Who did his exercises? _____

4. Who washed her face? _____

5. Who got dressed? _____

6. Who made the bed? _____

7. Who ate breakfast? _____

8. Who read the newspaper? _____

9. Who brushed his teeth? _____

10. Who put on her sweater? _____

11. Who kissed her family? _____

12. Who left the house? _____

VERB FORMS

Practice the pronunciation of these verb forms by repeating them after your teacher:

basic forms	stretch	yawn	rub	do	wash	wake
past forms	stretched	yawned	rubbed	did	washed	woke

get	make	eat	read	brush	put on	kiss	leave
got	made	ate	read	brushed	put on	kissed	left

Now go back and practice the questions and answers above with a classmate.

Carol

This morning Carol woke up at 7:00. She got up and did her exercises. After that she washed her face. Then she got dressed and made her bed. She ate breakfast and read the newspaper. Then she brushed her teeth. Carol put on her sweater and kissed her family goodbye. She left the house at 8:30.

You

Complete the answers to the questions about your personal activities this morning. Then practice the conversation with a classmate.

1. What time did you wake up this morning? I woke up at _____ .

2. What time did you get up? I got up at _____ .

3. Did you do your exercises?   Yes, I did.   No, I didn't.

4. Did you wash your face before or after you got dressed?

     I washed my face _____ I got dressed.

5. Did you make the bed? _____ .

6. Did you brush your teeth before or after breakfast?

     I brushed my teeth _____ breakfast.

7. What did you eat for breakfast today?

     I ate _____ for breakfast today.

8. Did you read the newspaper this morning? _____ .

9. What time did you leave the house? I left the house at _____ .

Crossword Puzzle

ACROSS

2. Make the _____ .
3. Read the _____ .
5. Rub your _____ .
7. Wash your _____ .
8. He's rubbing_____ eyes.
9. She's putting on _____ sweater.
10. I'm kissing _____ family.
11. They're brushing_____ teeth.
13. Leave the _____ .
14. Brush your_____ .
15. We're doing_____exercises.

DOWN

1. Kiss your _____ .
2. Eat _____ .
4. Do your _____ .
6. Put on your _____ .
12. You're washing _____ face.

DICTATION

SOUNDS OF ENGLISH

Listen to the teacher. Circle the word you hear.

1. yawn   John

2. yawn   young

3. rub   rubbed

4. exercise   exercises

5. wash   watch

6. kiss   keys

7. live   leave

8. it   eat

UNIT 2 TIME TO CLEAN HOUSE

1. Put on your apron.

2. Sprinkle some kitchen cleanser in the sink.

3. Scrub the sink with a sponge.

4. Sweep the kitchen floor with a broom.

5. Fill a bucket with water.

6. Put some liquid cleaner in it.

7. Stick the mop in it.

8. Mop the kitchen floor.

9. Dust the furniture with a dust cloth.

10. Empty the wastebaskets.

11. Plug in the vacuum cleaner.

12. Turn it on.

13. Vacuum the rugs and carpets.

14. Put all the cleaning stuff away.

15. Look around. It looks much better.

PRESENT PROGRESSIVE, LONG ANSWERS

Look at the photos and complete the answers with the *-ing* form of the verb:

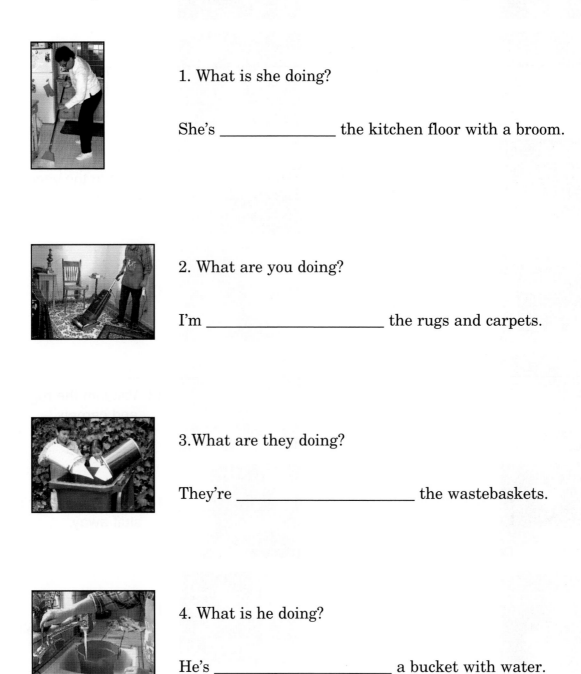

1. What is she doing?

She's _____ the kitchen floor with a broom.

2. What are you doing?

I'm _____ the rugs and carpets.

3. What are they doing?

They're _____ the wastebaskets.

4. What is he doing?

He's _____ a bucket with water.

5. What am I doing?

You're _____ the furniture with a dust cloth.

6. What are we doing?

We're _____ all the cleaning stuff away.

7. What is she doing?

She's _____ some kitchen cleanser in the sink.

8. What are you doing?

I'm _____ in the vacuum cleaner.

9. What are they doing?

They're _____ around.

QUESTIONS

Exercise 1
Point to a picture. Ask a classmate: **What do you call this?**

1.
2.
3.
4.

5.
6.
7.
8.

9.
10.
11.
12.

Exercise 2
Point to a word. Ask a classmate: **How do you pronounce this word?**

1. apron	2. sink	3. kitchen cleanser	4. sponge
5. broom	6. bucket	7. liquid cleaner	8. mop
9. furniture	10. dust cloth	11. wastebasket	12. vacuum cleaner

13. cleaning stuff

Exercise 3
Ask a classmate how to spell words from the list:
How do you spell "mop"?

Write the letters on a piece of paper as you listen to the spelling.

PREPOSITIONS

13.

Answer the questions about #13, the picture of the cleaning stuff.

Use the correct preposition:

in	on	under	next to	in front of	behind	between

1. Where is the apron?   It's _____ the vacuum cleaner.

2. Where is the vacuum cleaner?   It's _____ the wastebasket.

3. Where is the liquid cleaner?   It's _____ the wastebasket.

4. Where is the sponge?   It's _____ the sink.

5. Where is the bucket?   It's _____ the broom and the vacuum cleaner.

6. Where is the dust cloth?   It's _____ the kitchen cleanser.

7. Where is the wastebasket?   It's _____ the sink.

8. Where is the mop?   It's _____ the bucket.

9. Where is the bucket?   It's _____ the sink.

PRESENT TENSE CONVERSATION

Complete the answers with personal information about cleaning your house. Use these phrases of frequency:

every day	**once a week**	**once a month**
twice a day	**twice a week**	**twice a month**
three times a day	**three times a week**	**three times a month**

Then practice the conversation with a classmate.

1. How often do you sweep the kitchen floor?
   I sweep the kitchen floor _____ .

2. How often do you mop it?
   I mop it _____ .

3. How often do you scrub the kitchen sink?
   I scrub the kitchen sink _____ .

4. Do you put on an apron to clean house?
   a. Yes, I do.   b. No, I don't.

5. How often do you clean the bathroom?
   I clean the bathroom _____ .

6. How often do you dust the furniture?
   I dust the furniture _____ .

7. How often do you empty the wastebaskets?
   I empty the wastebaskets _____ .

8. How often do you vacuum?
   I vacuum _____ .

9. Do you like to clean house?
   a. Yes, I do.   b. No, I don't.

10. Is your house clean right now?
    a. Yes, it is.   b. No, it isn't.

> **Every Friday**
>
> Every Friday, Robert cleans his house. He scrubs the kitchen sink and sweeps the floor. He fills a bucket, sticks the mop in it, and mops the kitchen floor. He dusts the furniture and empties the wastebaskets. He turns on the vacuum cleaner and vacuums the carpets. After that, the house looks much better

1. Does Robert clean his house on Saturday?
    a. Yes, he does.
    b. No, he doesn't.

2. Does he scrub the sink before or after he sweeps the floor?

    He scrubs the sink _____ he sweeps the floor.

3. Does he mop the floor before or after he sweeps it?

    He mops the floor _____ he sweeps it.

4. Does he always dust the furniture?
    a. Yes, he does.
    b. No, he doesn't.

5. Does he empty the wastebaskets?
    a. Yes, he does.
    b. No, he doesn't.

6. How does he clean the carpets?

    He _____ the carpets.

7. How does the house look when he's finished?

    It _____ much better.

PAST TENSE

1. Who put on the apron? _____ did.

2. Who sprinkled some kitchen cleanser in the sink? _____ did.

3. Who scrubbed the sink with a sponge? _____

4. Who swept the floor? _____

5. Who filled the bucket with water? _____

6. Who put some liquid cleaner in it? _____

7. Who stuck the mop in it? _____

8. Who mopped the floor? _____

9. Who dusted the furniture? _____

10. Who emptied the wastebaskets? _____

11. Who plugged in the vacuum cleaner? _____

12. Who turned it on? _____

13. Who vacuumed the rugs and carpets? _____

14. Who put all the cleaning stuff away? _____

VERB FORMS

basic forms	put on	sprinkle	scrub	sweep	fill	stick
past forms	put on	sprinkled	scrubbed	swept	filled	stuck

mop	dust	empty	plug	turn on	vacuum	look
mopped	dusted	emptied	plugged	turned on	vacuumed	looked

Robert

Last Friday, Robert cleaned his house. He scrubbed the kitchen sink and swept the floor. He filled a bucket, stuck the mop in it, and mopped the kitchen floor. He dusted the furniture and emptied the wastebaskets. He turned on the vacuum cleaner and vacuumed the carpets. After that, the house looked much better.

Give short answers to these questions about Robert:

Yes, he did.   or   **No, he didn't.**

1. Did Robert clean his house last Friday?

2. Did he scrub the sink with a broom?

3. Did he mop the floor before he swept it?

4. Did he dust the furniture?

5. Did he fill the wastebaskets?

6. Did he mop the carpets?

7. Did he put all the cleaning stuff away?

RHYMES

On Page 11, find a word that rhymes with:

1. stop   _____   4. sleep   _____

2. mouse   _____   5. enough   _____

3. more   _____

Find two words that rhyme with:

6. perfume   _____   _____

7. hug   _____   _____

Crossword Puzzle

Refer to photo on page 20.

ACROSS

4.

5. The sponge is _____ the sink.

9.

11. _____ cleaner

12. cleaning _____

16.

DOWN

1.

2. The mop is ____ front of the sink.

3. The wastebasket is___ to the sink.

6.

7. Kitchen _____ .

8.   10.

13. The broom is in _____ of the dust cloth.

14.

15. The apron is_____ the vacuum cleaner.

DICTATION

UNIT 3   PLAYING A CASSETTE

1. Turn on the radio.

2. Switch to tape.

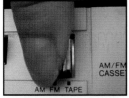

3. Press eject.

4. Stick the cassette in.

5. Press play.

6. That's not it! Fast-forward it.

7. OK. Hit play again.

8. Oh, no. It's on the other side.

9. Push stop and push it again.

10. Take the tape out.

11. Turn it over and put it back in.

12. Rewind it.

13. OK, try it here.

14. Oh good, this is it. Listen to this!

POWER

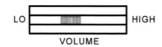
LO ▮▮▮ HIGH
VOLUME

TAPE   RADIO

RECORD   PLAY   REWIND   FAST-FORWARD   STOP/EJECT

PRESENT PROGRESSIVE, LONG ANSWERS

Complete the answers with the *-ing* form of the verb:

1. What is she doing?

   She's _____ stop.

2. What are you doing?

   I'm _____ the tape.

3. What are they doing?

   They're _____ to music.

4. What is he doing?

   He's _____ the tape over.

5. What am I doing?

   You're _____ it.

6. What is he doing?

   He's _____ play.

7. What is she doing?

   She's _____ on the radio.

8. What are you doing?

   I'm _____ the tape out.

Now Practice with a classmate. Point to a photo and ask the question. Check the answer.

Present Progressive

Ann and I are listening to music. I'm switching the radio to tape and sticking in a cassette. Now I'm pressing play, but this isn't the song I want. Ann is pressing fast-forward. Now she's hitting play. No good. Now we're turning the tape over and rewinding it. Ann is trying it here. Yes! This is the song!

PRESENT PROGRESSIVE, SHORT ANSWERS

Answer these questions about the story.
Use the correct form of the verb to be:

is	isn't	are	aren't

1. Are we listening to music?   Yes, we ____*are*____ .

2. Am I turning on the radio?   No, you _____ .

3. Is Ann sticking in a cassette?   No, she _____ .

4. Is she rewinding it?   No, she _____ .

5. Am I pressing play?   Yes, you _____ .

6. Am I pressing fast-forward?   No, you _____ .

7. Is Ann hitting play?   Yes, she _____ .

8. Are we turning the tape over?   Yes, we _____ .

9. Is Ann trying it here?   Yes, she _____ .

10. Is this the song?   Yes, it _____ !

Now practice with a classmate.

PRESENT TENSE CONVERSATION

**Complete the answers with personal information.
Then practice the conversation with a classmate.**

1. How often do you listen to the radio?

   I listen to the radio _____ .

2. How often do you watch TV?

   I watch TV _____ .

3. Do you listen to cassettes or CDs?

   a. Yes, I listen to _____ .
   b. No, I don't.

4. Do you listen to songs in English?

   a. Yes, I do.
   b. No, I don't.

5. Does your mother listen to songs in English?

   a. Yes, she does.
   b. No, she doesn't.

VERB FORMS

basic forms	play	turn on	switch	press	stick	fast-forward
past forms	played	turned on	switched	pressed	stuck	fast-forwarded

hit	push	take	turn over	put	rewind	try	listen
hit	pushed	took	turned over	put	rewound	tried	listened

Last Night

Last night Ann played a cassette. First she turned on the radio and switched to tape. She stuck in a cassette and pressed play. Then she fast-forwarded it and hit play again, but the song was on the other side. She took out the tape, turned it over and rewound it. Finally, she listened to her song. Then she was happy.

Yes, she did.   or   **No, she didn't.**

Give short answers to these questions about Ann:

1. Did Ann listen to the radio last night?

2. Did she switch to tape?

3. Did she stick in a cassette?

4. Did she press eject?

5. Did she fast-forward it?

6. Did she hit fast-forward again?

7. Did she take the tape out?

8. Did she rewind it?

9. Did she listen to her song?

SHORT ANSWERS, MIXED TENSES

Give short answers to these personal questions:

Yes, I am.   No, I'm not.

Yes, I do.   No, I don't.

Yes, I did.   No, I didn't.

1. Do you like music?

2. Do you listen to music every day?

3. Are you listening to music right now?

4. Are you dancing?

5. Did you listen to a cassette yesterday?

6. Did you listen to a CD last night?

7. Are you watching TV right now?

8. Do you watch TV every day?

9. Do you watch movies in English?

10. Did you watch movies in English last year?

RHYMES

On Page 23, find a word that rhymes with:

1. make _____ 5. find _____

2. yes _____ 6. past _____

3. mother _____ 7. then _____

4. my _____ 8. ear _____

9. day _____

Find two words that rhyme with:

10. sit _____ _____

Crossword Puzzle

ACROSS

1. try to hear
4. The opposite of rewind is fast- _____
6. stop for a short time
7. tape (noun)

DOWN

1. try to see
2. put it out
3. turn it back
6. push
8. change

DICTATION

UNIT 4

GROCERY SHOPPING

1. Go to the produce section.

8. Choose some eggs.

2. Choose some fruit.

9. That's enough food. Go to the checkout.

3. Put it in your cart.

10. Stand in line.

4. Choose some vegetables.

11. Say hello to the cashier.

5. Weigh them.

12. Pay him for your groceries.

6. That's too much. Put some back.

13. Wait for him to bag them.

7. Go to the dairy section.

14. Take the groceries to your car.

Present Progressive

Al and I are in the grocery store. We're choosing some fruit and vegetables. I'm weighing them and putting them in the cart. Now we're standing in line. I'm saying hello to the cashier and paying. Now we're waiting for him. He's bagging the groceries. Now I'm picking them up and we're going home.

PRESENT PROGRESSIVE, LONG ANSWERS

Complete the answers with the *-ing* form of the verb:

1. What are we doing?

We're _____ some fruit.

2. What are you doing?

I'm _____ them.

3. What are they doing?

They're _____ in line.

4. What is she doing?

She's _____ hello to the cashier.

5. What is he doing?

He's _____ the groceries.

6. What am I doing?

You're _____ for your groceries.

7. What are we doing?

We're _____ the groceries to our car.

PRESENT PROGRESSIVE
DON'T!

Example: Go to the produce section.

Don't *go* to the restroom!
I'm not *going* to the restroom.
Where are you *going*?
I'm going to the produce section.

1.   Choose some fruit.

Don't _____ some flowers.

I'm not _____ some flowers.

What are you _____ ?

I'm _____ some fruit.

2.   Put it in your cart.

Don't _____ it in your mouth!

I'm not _____ it in my mouth.

Where are you _____ it?

I'm _____ it in my cart.

3.   Weigh the vegetables.

Don't eat them.

I'm not _____ them.

What are you doing?

I'm _____ them.

4.   Stand in line.

Don't sit down.

I'm not _____ down.

What are you doing?

I'm _____ in line.

5.   Say hello to the cashier.

Don't _____ "I love you"!

I'm not _____ "I love you."

What are you _____ ?

I'm _____ hello.

6.   Pay for your groceries.

Don't _____ for cigarettes!

I'm not _____ for cigarettes.

What are you _____ for?

I'm _____ for my groceries.

7.   Wait for the cashier to bag them.

Don't _____ for him to cook them!

I'm _____ _____ for him to cook them.

What _____ you _____ for?

I'm _____ for him to bag them.

8.   Take your groceries to the car.

Don't _____ them to the garbage.

I'm _____ _____ them to the garbage.

Where _____ you _____ them?

I'm _____ them to my car.

PRESENT TENSE CONVERSATION

Complete the answers with personal information about shopping for groceries. Then practice the conversation with a classmate.

1. How often do you shop for groceries?

    I shop for groceries _____

2. How often do you buy fruit?

    I buy fruit _____

3. What kind of fruit do you like?

    I like _____

4. What kind of vegetables do you like?

    I like _____

5. What kind of dairy products do you buy?

    I buy _____

6. What other groceries do you buy?

    I buy _____

    _____

7. How much milk do you buy every week?

    I buy _____

8. How often do you buy chicken?

    I buy chicken _____

9. Do you like to shop for groceries?   a. Yes, I do.   b. No, I don't.

10. Do you go grocery shopping alone or with another person? (Who?)

    a. I go grocery shopping alone.

    b. I go grocery shopping with _____

VERB FORMS

basic forms	go	choose	put	weigh	stand	pick up
past forms	went	chose	put	weighed	stood	picked up
	say	wait	bag	take	pay	
	said	waited	bagged	took	paid	

Yesterday

Yesterday I went shopping. I chose some fruit and put it in my cart. Then I weighed some vegetables and put some back. I chose some eggs, too. Next I stood in line at the checkout. I said hello to the cashier and paid him. I waited while he bagged the groceries. Then I picked up the bag and went home.

Answer these questions about the story:

1. When did I go shopping? You _____

2. What did I choose? You _____

3. Where did I put it? You _____

4. What did I do with the vegetables?
   You_____them and_____ some back.

5. What else did I choose? You _____

6. What did I do then? You _____

7. What did I say to the cashier? You _____

8. Did I pay him? _____

9. What did I do while he bagged my groceries? You _____

10. Where did I go after I picked up my groceries? You _____

QUESTIONS

Exercise 1
Point to a picture. Ask a classmate: **What do you call this?**

1.

2.

3.

4.

5.

6.

7.

8.

9.

10.

11.

12.

13.

14.

15.

16.

17.

18.

Exercise 2
Point to a word.
Ask a classmate:
How do you pronounce this word?

1. green beans
5. yogurt
9. bananas
13. potato

2. apple
6. broccoli
10. peppers
14. spinach
17. cheese

3. eggs
7. orange
11. tomato
15. grapes
18. groceries

4. pineapple
8. milk
12. butter
16. strawberries

Exercise 3
Now ask a classmate: **How do you spell "strawberries"?**

Write the letters on a piece of paper as you listen to the spelling.

PREPOSITIONS

**Answer the questions about #18, the picture of the groceries on page 38.
Use the correct preposition:**

     on   under   next to   in front of   behind   between

1. Where are the peppers?   They're _____ the eggs.

2. Where is the cheese?   It's _____ the green beans.

3. Where is the milk?   It's _____ the cheese.

4. Where is the butter?   It's _____ the eggs.

5. Where is the spinach?   It's _____ the milk and the broccoli.

6. Where are the eggs?   They're _____ the yogurt.

7. Where is the potato?   It's _____ the yogurt.

8. Where is the broccoli?   It's _____ the eggs.

9. Where is the yogurt?   It's _____ the broccoli.

10. Where is the milk?   It's _____ the grapes.

11. Where are the apples?   They're _____ the bananas and the cheese.

12. Where are the green beans?   They're _____ the milk.

What kind of food is this?

Write the names of the groceries on page 38 in the correct lists below.

fruit	vegetables	dairy
_____	green beans	_____
_____	_____	_____
_____	_____	_____
_____	_____	_____
_____	_____	_____

RHYMES

On Page 31, find a word that rhymes with:

1. start _____   6. Mary _____

2. hand _____   7. election _____

3. flag _____   8. news _____

4. boot _____   9. here _____

5. yellow _____

Find three words that rhyme with:

10. day _____ _____ _____

Crossword Puzzle

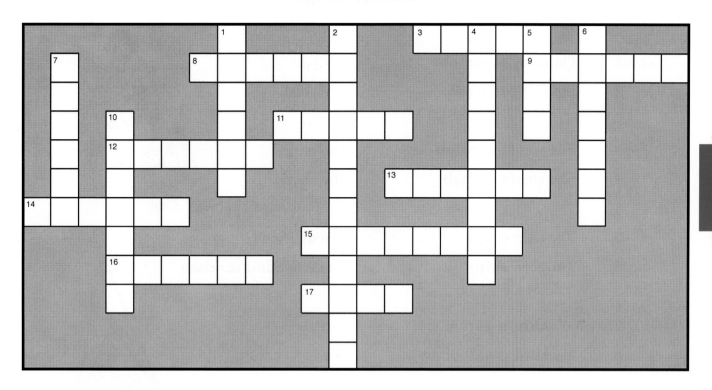

ACROSS

3.

8.

9.

11.

12.

13.

14.

15.

16.

17.

DOWN

1.

2.

4.

5.

6.

7.

10.

ch/sh Bingo

1.   I'm going to **watch**   TV.
2.   I'm going to **wash**   my shirt.

3.   She wants to **catch**   the ball.
4.   She wants to **cash**   the check.

5.   The corn **chips**   are delicious.
6.   The corn **ships**   came to San Francisco.

7.   My **chin** is part of my   face.
8.   My **shin** is part of my   leg.

9.   Are you going to **chop**   the vegetables?
10. Are you going to **shop**   for groceries?

11. I want my **chair**   to sit on.
12. I want my **share**   of the food.

13. I saw her **choose**   some eggs.
14. I saw her **shoes**   on the floor.

15. Will you please **match**   your socks?
16. Will you please **mash**   the potatoes?

UNIT 5   GIVING DIRECTIONS

1. Do you want to drive? I'll sit in the passenger seat.

8. Turn right at the stop sign.

2. It's that way. Turn around.

9. Hey, slow down.

3. Go up there to the light.

10. Go up the hill. It's near the top.

4. Turn left at the light.

11. Oh! We passed it. Back up.

5. Get on the freeway just past that sign.

12. Here it is. Look. It's across the street from the school.

6. I think it's the second exit. There it is — Carlson Boulevard. Get off here.

13. OK. Park here.

7. Go straight ahead for three blocks.

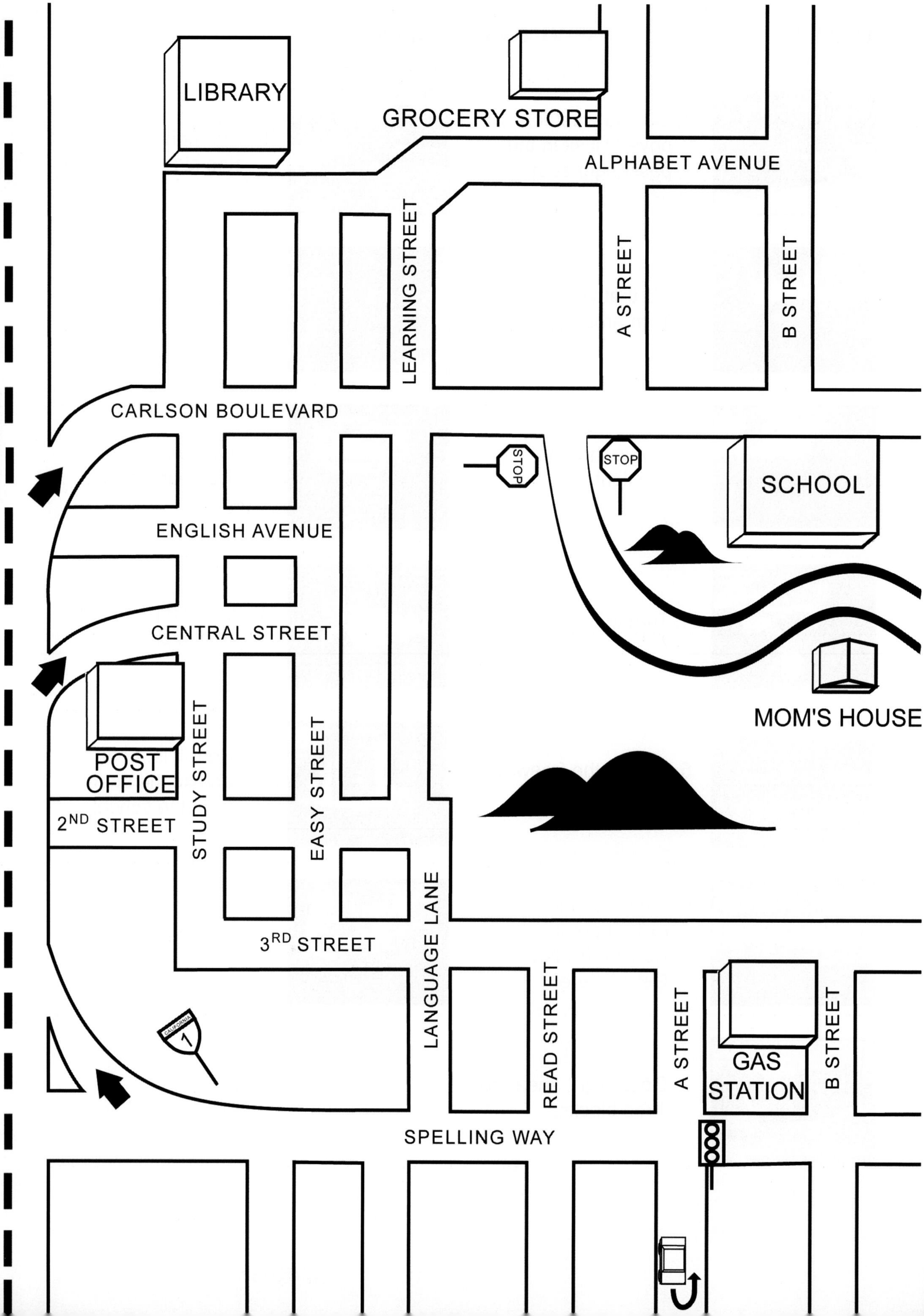

LIBRARY

GROCERY STORE

ALPHABET AVENUE

LEARNING STREET

A STREET

B STREET

CARLSON BOULEVARD

STOP

STOP

SCHOOL

ENGLISH AVENUE

CENTRAL STREET

MOM'S HOUSE

POST OFFICE

2ND STREET

STUDY STREET

EASY STREET

LANGUAGE LANE

3RD STREET

CALIFORNIA 1

READ STREET

A STREET

GAS STATION

B STREET

SPELLING WAY

WRITING DIRECTIONS

Look at the map on page 44. Write the directions from Mom's house to the library:

_____

_____

_____

_____

_____

_____

_____

_____

_____

_____

_____

SPELLING *-ing* FORMS

Write the *-ing* forms of these verbs:

Example: go _____*going*_____

1.	back up	_____	29.	put back	_____
2.	brush	_____	30.	put on	_____
3.	choose	_____	31.	read	_____
4.	do	_____	32.	rewind	_____
5.	drive	_____	33.	rub	_____
6.	dust	_____	34.	say	_____
7.	eat	_____	35.	scrub	_____
8.	empty	_____	36.	slow down	_____
9.	fast-forward	_____	37.	sprinkle	_____
10.	fill	_____	38.	stand	_____
11.	get dressed	_____	39.	stick	_____
12.	get off	_____	40.	stretch	_____
13.	get on	_____	41.	sweep	_____
14.	get up	_____	42.	switch	_____
15.	hit	_____	43.	take	_____
16.	kiss	_____	44.	take out	_____
17.	leave	_____	45.	think	_____
18.	listen	_____	46.	try	_____
19.	look	_____	47.	turn around	_____
20.	make	_____	48.	turn on	_____
21.	mop	_____	49.	turn over	_____
22.	park	_____	50.	vacuum	_____
23.	pass	_____	51.	wait	_____
24.	pay	_____	52.	wake up	_____
25.	plug in	_____	53.	want	_____
26.	press	_____	54.	wash	_____
27.	push	_____	55.	weigh	_____
28.	put away	_____	56.	yawn	_____

> ## Present, Present Progressive
> It's Sunday and we're going to Mom's house. We go every Sunday. Ted drives and I sit in the passenger seat. Right now we're getting on the freeway. Here's the exit. We're getting off. We're turning right. Now we're backing up. We always back up because Ted always passes it. OK. Now we're parking. Hi, Mom!

1. What day is it? _____

2. Where are they going? _____

3. How often do they go? _____

4. Who drives? _____

5. Where does the other person sit? _____

6. Are they getting on the freeway? _____

7. Do they turn right when they get off the freeway? _____

8. How often do they back up? _____

9. Why do they back up? _____

_____

10. Where are they parking? _____

_____

VERB FORMS

basic forms	drive	want	think	sit	turn	go	get
past forms	drove	wanted	thought	sat	turned	went	got

	slow	pass	back	look	park
	slowed	passed	backed	looked	parked

Past Tense: Last Sunday

Last Sunday we went to Mom's house. Ted drove and I sat in the passenger seat. We got on the freeway and got off at Carlson Boulevard. Then we turned right and went up the hill. We backed up because we passed Mom's house. We parked across the street from the school.

---

1. When did we go to Mom's house? You _____

2. Who drove? _____

3. Where did I sit? You _____

4. Where did we get off the freeway? _____

5. Did we turn left or right? You _____

6. Did we go up the hill or down the hill? You _____

7. Why did we back up? You _____

8. Where did we park? You _____

RHYMES

On Page 43 find a word that rhymes with:

1. wait _____

2. line _____

3. chair _____

4. boss _____

5. dark _____

6. Bill _____

7. dust _____

8. five _____

9. say _____

10. learn _____

Find two words that rhyme with:

11. no _____ _____

12. night _____ _____

13. beer _____ _____

14. meet _____ _____

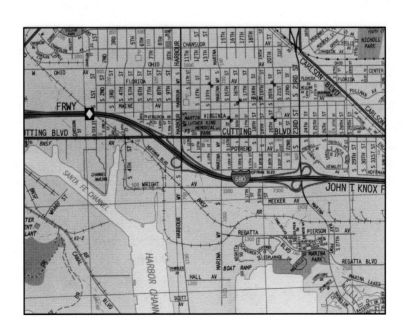

Crossword Puzzle

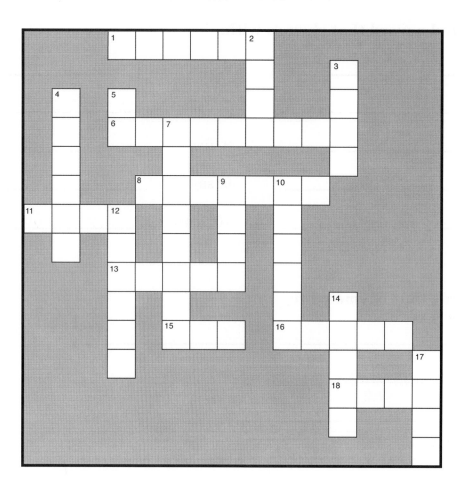

ACROSS

1. It's on the other side of the street; it's _____ the street.
6. a person in the car who is not the driver
8. a road where cars go very fast
11. a place to sit
13. opposite of left
15. opposite of bottom
16. control a car
18. Go up the _____ .

DOWN

2. You have to stop when you see a stop _____ .
3. Where did you _____ the car?
4. She _____ up the car. (past form)
5. opposite of down
7. Don't turn. Go _____ ahead.
9. a place to get off the freeway
10. If you need to go the other way, you can turn _____ .
12. past form of turn
14. You have to stop when you see a red _____ .
17. If you're going too fast, you have to _____ down.

SHORT ANSWERS — PERSONAL QUESTIONS

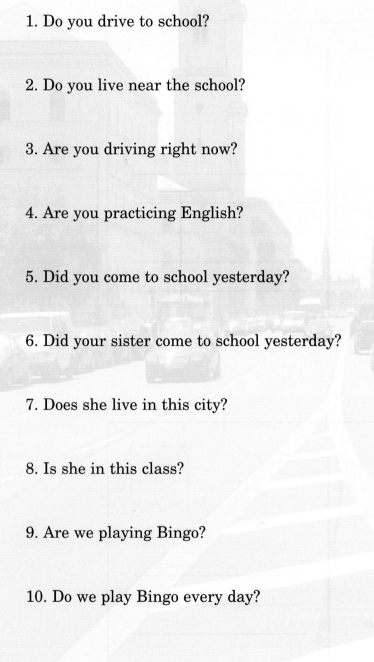

1. Do you drive to school?

2. Do you live near the school?

3. Are you driving right now?

4. Are you practicing English?

5. Did you come to school yesterday?

6. Did your sister come to school yesterday?

7. Does she live in this city?

8. Is she in this class?

9. Are we playing Bingo?

10. Do we play Bingo every day?

POST CARD

POST CARD

UNIT 6　　　SENDING A POSTCARD

 1. You are visiting San Francisco.

 2. Take pictures and enjoy the view.

 3. Find a shop that sells postcards.

 4. Choose a pretty one.

 5. Sit down and write your card.

 6. Write the date at the top.

 7. Write the message.

 8. Sign your name at the bottom.

 9. Write your friend's name and address on the card.

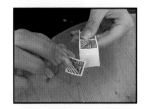 10. Tear off the stamp.

 11. Put the stamp in the right place.

 12. Take the postcard to the mailbox.

 13. Mail it.

VOCABULARY

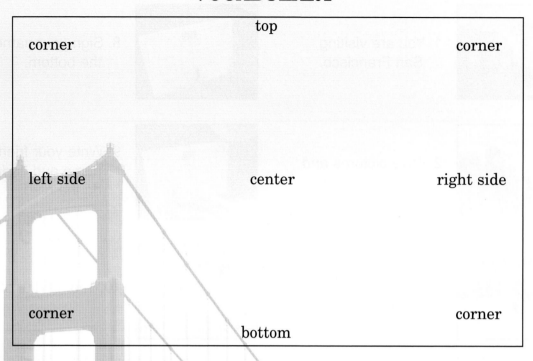

top

corner   corner

left side   center   right side

corner   corner

bottom

Listen to your partner. Point to the postcard *on the next page* to follow the instructions:

1. Point to the **center** of the card.

2. Point to the **corner** of the card.

3. Point to the **top** of the card.

4. Point to the **bottom** of the card.

5. Point to the **right side** of the card.

6. Point to the **left side** of the card.

Complete the answers. Then practice with a classmate.

1. Where are you going to put the stamp? In the _____ .

2. Where are you going to write the date?

      At the _____ of the card on the _____ side.

3. Where are you going to write the address? On the _____ side.

4. Where are you going to sign your name?

      At the _____ of the message on the _____ side.

Post Card

PRESENT PROGRESSIVE
DON'T!

Example: Take pictures.

Don't _Take_ a break!

I'm not _Taking_ a break.

What are you _Taking_?

I'm _Taking_ pictures.

1.   Find a shop that sells postcards.

Don't _____ a shop that sells beer!

I'm not _____ a shop that sells beer.

What are you _____ ?

I'm _____ a shop that sells postcards.

2.   Choose a pretty card.

Don't _____ an ugly card!

I'm not _____ an ugly card.

What are you _____ ?

I'm _____ a pretty card.

3.   Sit down.

Don't stand up.

I'm not _____ up.

What are you doing?

I'm _____ down.

4.   Write the date at the top.

Don't _____ it at the bottom.

I'm not _____ it at the bottom.

Where are you _____ it?

I'm _____ it at the top.

5.   Sign your name at the bottom.

Don't _____ it at the top!

I'm not _____ it at the top.

Where are you _____ it?

I'm _____ it at the bottom.

6.   Tear off a stamp.

Don't _____ off a paper towel!

I'm not _____ off a paper towel.

What are you _____ off?

I'm _____ off a stamp.

7.   Take the postcard to the mailbox.

Don't _____ it home!

I'm _____ _____ it home.

Where _____ you _____ it?

I'm _____ it to the mailbox.

8.   Mail it.

Don't throw it away.

I'm _____ _____ it away.

What _____ you _____ ?

I'm _____ it.

Now practice with a classmate.

Present Tense

Bob's cousins love San Francisco and visit there every year. They usually take pictures and enjoy the beautiful views. Then they find a shop that sells postcards. They always choose a pretty one for Bob and write him a message. After they sign it at the bottom, they tear off a stamp and put it on the card. Then they take the postcard to the mailbox and mail it to him.

1. Why do Bob's cousins visit San Francisco every year?

 They visit San Francisco every year because they _____ it there.

2. What do they usually do there?

 They usually _____ pictures and _____ the views.

3. What do they find there? They _____ a shop that sells postcards.

4. Do they sometimes choose an ugly postcard for Bob?

 No, they always _____ a pretty one.

5. Where do they sign it? They _____ it at the bottom.

6. How many stamps do they tear off? They _____ off one stamp.

7. Where do they take the postcard? They _____ it to a mailbox.

8. Who do they mail it to? They _____ it to Bob.

9. When you go to a new place, do you take pictures of the views?

 a. Yes, I do.   b. No, I don't.

10. Do you send postcards to your friends? _____ .

11. What city do you love to visit? I love to visit _____ .

> ### Future Tense
> Next week Christina, a student, is going to visit San Francisco. On Monday she is going to take pictures and enjoy the views. On Tuesday she'll find a shop that sells postcards. She'll choose a pretty one. The following day she'll write the postcard, sign it, and put a stamp on it. After that she's going to mail it.

1. When is Christina going to visit San Francisco? She _____

_____ next week.

2. What is she going to do on Monday? She _____

_____

3. What will she find on Tuesday? She _____

_____

4. What will she choose? She _____

5. What will she do on Wednesday? She _____

_____

6. What is she going to do after that? She _____

_____

VERB FORMS

basic forms	visit	take	enjoy	find	sell	choose	sit
past forms	visited	took	enjoyed	found	sold	chose	sat

	write	sign	tear	put	mail		
	wrote	signed	tore	put	mailed		

Past Tense: Last Week...

Last week Christina visited San Francisco. She took some pictures and enjoyed the views. She found a shop that sold postcards and chose a pretty one. She wrote a message and signed her name at the bottom. Then she tore off a stamp and put it on the postcard. She took the card to a mailbox and mailed it.

1. Which city did Christina visit last week? She _____

2. What did she do there? She _____

3. What did she find? She _____

4. What did she choose? She _____

5. What did she write? She _____

6. Where did she sign her name? She _____

7. What did she tear off? She _____

8. Where did she mail it? She _____ it from a mailbox.

FOUR TENSES

Complete each question with the correct time phrase. Then give a short answer.

every year   next year   last year   right now

1. Did you visit San Francisco _____*last year*_____ ? _____*No, I didn't.*_____

2. Do you visit San Francisco _____ ? _____

3. Are you visiting San Francisco _____ ? _____

4. Are you going to visit San Francisco _____ ? _____

at this moment   yesterday   tomorrow   every day

5. Did Christina take pictures _____ ? _____

6. Does Christina take pictures _____ ? _____

7. Is Christina taking pictures _____ ? _____

8. Is Christina going to take pictures _____ ? _____

every time he's on vacation   the last time he was on vacation

the next time he's on vacation   at this moment

9. Did he mail you a card _____ ? _____

10. Does he mail you a card _____ ? _____

11. Is he mailing you a card _____ ? _____

12. Will he mail you a card _____ ? _____

A POSTCARD TO YOUR FRIENDS OR FAMILY

Now write a postcard to someone in your country.
Write the date at the top.
Tell them something about the city you are in now.
Sign it at the bottom.
Write their address in the right place.
Tear off a stamp.
Put it in the right place.

POST CARD

POST CARD

RHYMES

On Page 53, find a word that rhymes with:

1. wait _____

2. night _____

3. city _____

4. hard _____

5. sale _____

6. boy _____

7. fine _____

8. chair _____

9. lamp _____

10. two _____

Find two words that rhyme with:

11. stop _____   _____

Crossword Puzzle

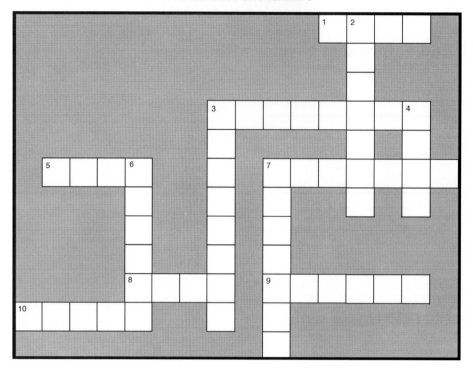

ACROSS

1. month, day, year
3. photographs
5. store
7. note
8. "break" paper
9. opposite of top
10. have a good time

DOWN

2. house number, street, city, state, country
3. a card to send in the mail
4. write your name in your personal way
6. beautiful
7. Where did you put the postcard?

UNIT 7 GOING FISHING

1. Find a good place.

7. Wait for the fish to bite.

2. Put your fishing pole together.

8. Have something to eat.

3. Tie a weight to the end of the line.

9. The pole moved! Pull it in!

4. Tie a hook above the weight.

10. It's too small. Throw it back in the water.

5. Put some bait on the hook.

11. Try again.

6. Throw your line in the water.

12. Hey! You got one. This one is big.

PRESENT PROGRESSIVE, LONG ANSWERS

Complete the answers with the *-ing* form of the verb:

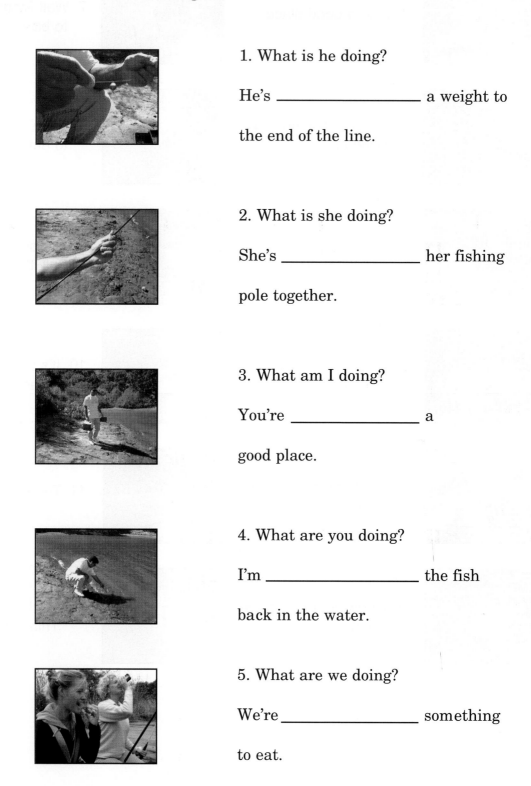

1. What is he doing?

He's _____ a weight to

the end of the line.

2. What is she doing?

She's _____ her fishing

pole together.

3. What am I doing?

You're _____ a

good place.

4. What are you doing?

I'm _____ the fish

back in the water.

5. What are we doing?

We're _____ something

to eat.

6. What is he doing?

He's _____ a hook

above the weight.

7. What are they doing?

They're _____ for the

fish to bite.

8. What am I doing?

You're _____

in a fish.

9. What is he doing?

He's _____ his

line in the water.

10. What are you doing?

I'm _____ some bait

on the hook.

Now practice with a classmate.

SOUNDS OF ENGLISH

Listen to teacher pronounce one word. Circle the letter of the word you hear:

1. a. pull   b. pole   c. pool

2. a. pull   b. pole   c. pool

3. a. pull   b. pole   c. pool

4. a. bit   b. bite   c. bait   d. beat

5. a. bit   b. bite   c. bait   d. beat

6. a. bit   b. bite   c. bait   d. beat

7. a. bit   b. bite   c. bait   d. beat

8. a. something   b. same thing

9. a. something   b. same thing

10. a. tea   b. tie   c. try   d. tree

11. a. tea   b. tie   c. try   d. tree

12. a. tea   b. tie   c. try   d. tree

13.   a. tea   b. tie   c. try   d. tree

14.   a. find   b. fine   c. fin

15.   a. find   b. fine   c. fin

16.   a. find   b. fine   c. fin

17.   a. weight   b. way   c. waited

18.   a. weight   b. way   c. waited

19.   a. weight   b. way   c. waited

20.   a. hook   b. hawk   c. who   d. how

21.   a. hook   b. hawk   c. who   d. how

22.   a. hook   b. hawk   c. who   d. how

23.   a. hook   b. hawk   c. who   d. how

QUESTIONS

1. Point to an object. Ask a classmate: What do you call this?

2. Point to a word. Ask a classmate: How do you pronounce this word?

a. water   b. line   c. pole   d. hook   e. weight   f. bait   g. float

3. Now ask a classmate: How do you spell "line"?

PREPOSITIONS

Answer the questions about the picture on page 70.
Use the correct preposition:

in	on	above	below	between

1. Where is the float?   It's _____ the water.

2. Where is the fishing pole?   It's _____ the water.

3. Where is the hook?   It's _____ the water.

4. Where is the weight?   It's _____ the hook.

5. Where is the bait?   It's _____ the hook.

6. Where is the hook?   It's _____ the weight and the float.

7. Which things are above the water? _____

8. Which things are on the water? _____

9. Which things are in the water? _____

10. Which things are on the line? _____

Future

Alex's going to go fishing tomorrow. He'll find a good place. He'll put his pole together and tie a weight and a hook to the line. Then he'll put some bait on the hook and throw his line in the water. When the pole moves, he'll pull it in. If the fish is too small, he'll throw it back. But he's going to get a big one!

---

1. When is Alex going to go fishing? He _____

_____

2. What will he do after he finds a good place? He _____

_____

3. What else will he do before he throws his line in the water? He _____

_____

4. What will he do when the pole moves? He _____

5. What will he do if the fish is too small? He _____

_____

6. Is he going to get a big one? _____

DICTATION: FUTURE TENSE

VERB FORMS

basic forms	find	put	tie	throw	wait	have
past forms	found	put	tied	threw	waited	had
	move	pull	try	get		
	moved	pulled	tried	got		

DICTATION: PAST TENSE

Past Tense: ...this morning

Alex went fishing this morning. He found a good place. He put his pole together and tied a weight and a hook to the line. He put some bait on the hook and threw his line in the water. When the pole moved, he pulled it in. The fish was too small, so he threw it back and tried again. He finally got a big one.

---

1. When did Alex go fishing? He _____

2. What did he find? He _____

3. What did he tie to his line? He _____

4. What did he put on the hook? He _____

5. Where did he throw his line? He _____

6. When did he pull it in? He _____ when the pole moved.

7. Why did he throw the fish back? He _____ because it was too small.

8. What did he get when he tried again? He _____

FOUR TENSES

Complete each question with the correct time phrase. Then give a short answer.

---

right now	next week	last week	every week

1. Did you go fishing ___*last week*___ ? _____*No, I didn't.*_____

2. Do you go fishing _____ ? _____

3. Are you fishing _____ ? _____

4. Are you going to go fishing _____ ? _____

---

in a few minutes	a few minutes ago	every time a fish bites	right now

5. Did the pole move _____ ? _____

6. Does the pole move _____ ? _____

7. Is the pole moving _____ ? _____

8. Will the pole move _____ ? _____

---

before class every day	before class today	after class today	at this moment

9. Did Alex have something to eat _____ ? _____

10. Does Alex have something to eat _____ ? _____

11. Is Alex having something to eat _____ ? _____

12. Is Alex going to have something to eat _____ ? _____

a/e/i BINGO

1.   **A** is the first letter of the word   America.

2.   **E** is the first letter of the word   English.

3.   **I** is the first letter of the word   India.

4.   Take the **bait**   to catch some fish.

5.   Take the **beet**   to the kitchen.

6.   Take the **bite**   of apple to the garbage.

7.   I'm waiting for a little **whale**   to pass my boat.

8.   I'm waiting for a little **wheel**   for my bike.

9.   I'm waiting for a little **while**   longer.

10. You told **May**   to come to school.

11. You told **me**   NO.

12. You told **my**   sister YES.

13. Do you have a **paint**   brush?

14. Do you have a **pint**   of milk?

15. My mother is **weeping**   because she's sad.

16. My mother is **wiping**   the table.

UNIT 8

USING A PAY PHONE

1. Find a pay phone.

2. Check the coin return. (nothing)

3. Pick up the receiver.

4. Take out the correct change.

5. Stick it in the slot.

6. Listen for the dial tone . . . Do you hear it?

7. Dial the number.

8. It's busy. Hang up.

9. Get your money back.

10. Wait a few minutes.

11. Read a book.

12. Try again.

13. OK, good. It's ringing.

14. Talk to your friend.

PRESENT PROGRESSIVE
DON'T!

Example: Stick the change in the slot.

Don't _stick_ it in your mouth!

I'm not _sticking_ it in my mouth.

Where are you _sticking_ it?

I'm _sticking_ it in the slot.

1.   Listen for the dial tone.

Don't _____ _____ music.

I'm not _____ _____ music.

What are you _____ _____ ?

I'm _____ _____ the dial tone.

2.   Dial your friend's number.

Don't _____ your zip code!

I'm not _____ my zip code.

What are you _____ ?

I'm _____ my friend's number.

3.   Get your money back.

_____ forget your money!

I'm _____ _____ my money.

What are you doing?

I'm _____ _____ my money back.

4.   Wait a few minutes.

_____   _____ an hour!

I'm _____   _____ an hour.

_____ are you doing?

_____   _____ a few minutes.

5.   Read a book.

_____   _____ the newspaper!

_____   _____   _____ the newspaper.

What _____   _____   _____ ?

_____   _____ a book.

6.   Talk to your friend.

_____ hang up!

_____ .

_____ ?

_____ .

Present, Present Progressive

When Maria finds a pay phone, she always checks the coin return. Then she picks up the receiver, sticks the change in the slot and dials the number. She's dialing right now, but it's busy, so she's hanging up. Now she's getting her money back and trying again. Oh! It's ringing! Now she's talking to her friend. They always talk for hours.

---

1. What does Maria do when she finds a pay phone? She _____

_____

2. What does she do after she picks up the receiver? She _____

_____

3. What is she doing right now? She _____

4. Why is she hanging up? She _____ because _____

5. What is she doing now? She _____

6. How long do they always talk? They _____

Past Tense: A few minutes ago...

A few minutes ago Maria found a pay phone. She checked the coin return. She picked up the receiver and stuck the change in the slot. Then she dialed the number, but it was busy so she hung up. She got her money back and waited. Then she tried again. This time it rang and she talked to her friend.

1. When did Maria find a pay phone? She _____

_____

2. What did she check? She _____

3. What did she pick up? She _____

4. Where did she stick the change? She _____

5. Why did she hang up? She _____ because _____

6. What did she do after she got her money back? She _____

7. What happened when she tried again? The phone _____

8. Who did she talk to? She _____

AFFIRMATIVE, NEGATIVE
PAST TENSE

Complete each sentence with the correct form of the verb(s):

Example: What did Maria find?   She *found* a pay phone.

What did Marlon find?   Marlon didn't *find* anything.

1. What did she check?   She _____ the coin return.

   What did he check?   He didn't _____ anything.

2. What did she pick up?   She _____ the receiver.

   What did he pick up?   He didn't _____ anything.

3. How much change did she take out?   She _____ 25 cents.

   How much did he take out?   He didn't _____ any.

4. Where did she stick it?   She _____ it in the slot.

   Where did he stick it?   He didn't _____ it anywhere.

5. What did she listen for?   She _____ for the dial tone.

   What did he listen for?   He didn't _____ for anything.

6. What number did she dial?   She _____ her friend's number.

   What number did he dial?   He didn't _____ any number.

7. Why did she hang up?   She _____ up because it was busy.

   Why did he hang up?   He didn't _____ up.

8. What did she get back?   She _____ her money back.

   What did he get back?   He didn't _____ anything back.

9. How long did she wait?   She _____ a few minutes.

   How long did he wait?   He didn't _____ .

10. What did she read?   She _____ a book.

    What did he read?   He didn't _____ anything.

11. When did she try again?   She _____ again in a few minutes.

    When did he try again?   He didn't _____ again.

12. How long did she talk to her friend? She _____ for half an hour.

    How long did he talk to his friend? He didn't _____ to his friend.

VERB FORMS

basic forms	find	check	pick up	take out	hear
past forms	found	checked	picked up	took out	heard
	stick	listen	dial	hang up	get
	stuck	listened	dialed	hung up	got
	wait	read	try	ring	talk
	waited	read	tried	rang	talked

PHONE DIALOGS

1.   Rrrrring!

Laura: Hello?
Paul: Hello, is this Laura?
Laura: Yes, it is.
Paul: Hi, Laura, this is Paul.
Laura: Oh, hi, Paul.

2.   Rrrrring!

Dora: Hello?
Paul: Hi, is this Laura?
Dora: No, it isn't. Just a minute, I'll get her.

3.   Rrrrring!

Laura: Hello?
Paul: Hello, is Laura there?
Laura: This is Laura. Who's this?
Paul: Oh, hi, Laura, this is Paul.

4.   Rrrrring!

Dora: Hello?
Paul: Hi, is Laura there?
Dora: Yes, may I ask who's calling?
Paul: This is Paul.
Dora: OK, hang on.

5.   Rrrrring!

Dora: Hello?
Paul: Hi, is Laura there?
Dora: No, she's not. Can I take a message?
Paul: Yes, please tell her Paul called.
Dora: OK, what's your number?
Paul: 555-9304. When will she be back?
Dora: She'll be back in about half an hour.
Paul: OK, I'll try again later. Thanks.
Dora: OK, goodbye.

6.

Rrrrring!

Dora:	Hello?
Paul:	Hi, is Laura there?
Dora:	No, she's not here right now.
Paul:	Can I leave a message?
Dora:	Sure, who's this?
Paul:	This is Paul, and the number is 555-9304.
Dora:	OK, I'll tell her.
Paul:	OK, thanks.
Dora:	Goodbye.

7.

Rrrrring!

John:	Hello?
Paul:	Hi, is Laura there?
John:	Sorry, you have a wrong number.
Paul:	Is this 555-7651?
John:	Yes, but there's no Laura here.
Paul:	OK, sorry to bother you.

RHYMES

On Page 79, find a word that rhymes with:

1. hot   _____   5. elect   _____

2. mile   _____   6. eight   _____

3. singing _____   7. then   _____

4. walk   _____   8. buy   _____

Find two words that rhyme with:

9. loan   _____   _____

m/n/ng BINGO

1.   Look at her **ham**   and eggs.

2.   Look at her **hand**   waving goodbye.

3.   Look at her **hang**   up the phone.

4.   That's the first **rum**   I ever drank.

5.   That's the first **run**   of the season.

6.   That's the first **rung**   of the ladder.

7.   We have three **Tums**   for our stomachaches.

8.   We have three **tons**   of sand from the beach.

9.   We have three **tongues**   to speak English.

10.   That's a funny **thin**   man.

11.   That's a funny **thing**   to say.

12.   My **Kim**   is a wonderful girl.

13.   My **kin**   are my family.

14.   My **king**   is very rich.

15.   Keep the **gum**   in your mouth!

16.   Keep the **gun**   away from me!

UNIT 9 PLANTING A SEED

1. Dig a hole in the ground.

2. Drop a tomato seed in it.

3. Cover the seed with soil.

4. Water it.

5. The plant is dry. Water it.

6. Wait for the plant to grow flowers.

7. Watch the tomatoes grow from the flowers.

8. Watch them turn red.

9. Pick a tomato.

10. Eat it. Mmmm! Can I have one?

PRESENT PROGRESSIVE, LONG ANSWERS

Complete the answers with the *-ing* form of the verb:

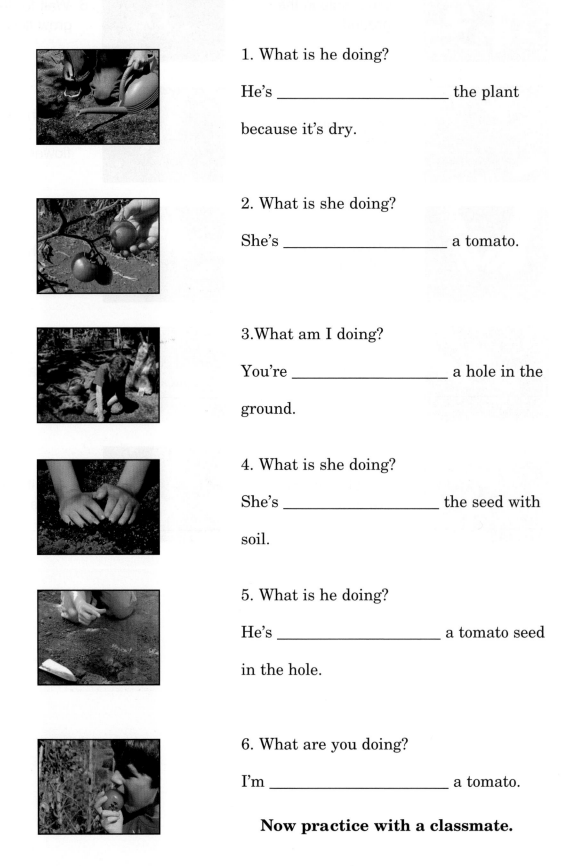

1. What is he doing?

He's _____ the plant

because it's dry.

2. What is she doing?

She's _____ a tomato.

3. What am I doing?

You're _____ a hole in the

ground.

4. What is she doing?

She's _____ the seed with

soil.

5. What is he doing?

He's _____ a tomato seed

in the hole.

6. What are you doing?

I'm _____ a tomato.

Now practice with a classmate.

PRESENT PROGRESSIVE, SHORT ANSWERS

1. Are we waiting for the plants to grow

flowers? _____

2. Are they watching the tomatoes turn red?

_____

3. Am I covering the seed with soil?

_____

4. Are you watering the plant?

_____

5. Is he eating a tomato?

_____

6. Is he digging a hole in the ground?

_____

7. Is he dropping a tomato seed in the hole?

_____

> ## Present Progressive, Future
> Look. Nick is planting a seed. He's digging a hole and dropping a seed in it. Now he's covering it and watering it. In a few weeks it'll grow into a tomato plant. He's going to water it and wait for it to grow flowers. The tomatoes are going to grow from the flowers. They'll turn red and he'll eat one.

1. What is Nick planting? He's _____

_____

2. Where is he digging a hole? He's _____

_____

3. What is he dropping in the hole? He's _____

_____

4. What is he covering it with? He's _____

5. When will the seed grow into a tomato plant? It'll _____

_____

6. What is he going to do while he waits for it to grow flowers? He's _____

_____

7. Where will the tomatoes grow? They'll _____

8. What color will they turn? They'll _____

9. How many will he eat? He'll _____

PERSONAL QUESTIONS

Answer these questions about yourself.

1. Do you have a garden? _____

2. Did you have a garden in your country? _____

3. Do you like to grow vegetables? _____

4. What kind of vegetables do you like to grow? _____

_____

5. Do you like to grow flowers? _____

6. What kind of flowers do you like to grow? _____

_____

VERB FORMS

basic forms	plant	dig	drop	cover
past forms	planted	dug	dropped	covered
	water	wait	watch	
	watered	waited	watched	
	grow	turn	pick	eat
	grew	turned	picked	ate

Past Tense: Last May...

Last May Nick planted a tomato seed. First he dug a hole and dropped the seed in it. Next he covered it with soil and watered it. It grew into a tomato plant. He waited for it to grow flowers. He watched tomatoes grow from the flowers. Then they turned red. Today he picked a tomato and ate it. Mmmm.

1. When did Nick plant the tomato seed? He _____

_____

2. What did he do first? He _____

_____

3. Where did he drop the seed? He _____

_____

4. What did he cover it with? He _____

_____

5. What did he do next? He _____

6. What happened to the seed? It _____

7. What happened to the flowers? They _____

8. What color did the tomatoes turn? They _____

9. What did Nick do today? He _____

AFFIRMATIVE, NEGATIVE
PAST TENSE

Complete each sentence with the correct form of the verb(s):

Example: What did Elsa dig?   She _dug_ a hole.

What did David dig?   He didn't _dig_ anything.

1. What did she drop in the hole?   She_____ a tomato seed in it.

   What did David drop in the hole?   He didn't_____ anything.

2. What did she cover it with?   She_____ it with soil.

   What did David cover it with?   He didn't_____ it with anything.

3. Why did she water it?   She_____ it because it was dry.

   Why did he water it?   He didn't_____ it.

4. What did she wait for?   She_____for the plant to grow flowers.

   What did he wait for?   He didn't_____ for anything.

5. What did she watch?   She_____ the tomatoes grow.

   What did he watch?   He didn't_____ anything.

6. What did she pick?   She_____ a tomato.

   What did he pick?   He didn't_____ anything.

7. What did she eat?   She_____ the tomato.

   What did he eat?   He didn't_____ anything.

FOUR TENSES

Complete each question with the correct time phrase. Then give a short answer.

every year	this year	next year	last year

1. Did you grow tomatoes ____*last year*____ ?   *No, I didn't.*

2. Do you grow tomatoes _____ ? _____

3. Are you growing tomatoes _____ ? _____

4. Are you going to grow tomatoes _____ ? _____

a few hours ago	in a few hours	every time it's dry	right now

5. Did Elsa water the plant _____ ? _____

6. Does Elsa water the plant _____ ? _____

7. Is Elsa watering the plant _____ ? _____

8. Will Elsa water the plant _____ ? _____

every month	next month	last month	at this time

9. Did we watch the tomatoes turn red _____ ? _____

10. Do we watch the tomatoes turn red _____ ? _____

11. Are the tomatoes turning red _____ ? _____

12. Will the tomatoes turn red _____ ? _____

BINGO!

UNIT 10   **MAKING A TABLE**

 1. Make a drawing of your table.

 2. Choose some nice boards.

 3. Take out your tape measure.

 4. Measure and mark the boards where you want to cut them.

 5. Draw a line across each board.

 6. Saw through each board.

 7. Get out your hammer and nails.

 8. Make a frame.

 9. Nail the top to the frame.

 10. Pound the nails all the way in.

 11. Turn it upside down.

 12. Nail the legs to the corners.

 13. Turn it over. Hey, that's a nice table!

 14. You're a great carpenter!

PRESENT PROGRESSIVE, LONG ANSWERS

Complete the answers:

1. What is he doing?

He's _____ the board.

2. What is he measuring it with?

He's _____ it with a

_____ .

3. What am I doing?

You're _____ through the board.

4. What am I sawing with?

You're _____ with a

_____ .

5. What is she doing?

She's _____ the nails all

the way in.

6. What is she pounding them with?

She's _____ them

with a _____ .

7. What is he doing?

_____

_____

8. What am I doing?

_____

_____

9. What are you doing?

_____

_____

10. What is he doing?

_____

_____

Now practice with a classmate.

MATERIALS

glass	wood	cloth	wax	metal
wool	paper	leather	plastic	wire

Select the correct material to answer each question:

1. What is the table made of?   _____

2. What are cars made of?   _____

3. What is your notebook made of?   _____

4. What are windows made of?   _____

5. What are your shoes made of?   _____

6. What is your comb made of?   _____

7. What are candles made of?   _____

8. What is your shirt made of?   _____

9. What is the coat hanger made of?   _____

10. What is your sweater made of?   _____

Past, Present Progressive, Future

Yesterday you made a drawing. Then you chose some boards. You measured and marked them where you wanted to cut them. Now you're sawing through each one. You're making the frame and nailing the top to it. Next you'll turn it upside down. Then you're going to nail the legs to the corners. It's going to be a nice table.

---

1. When did you make a drawing? I _____

2. What did you choose? I _____

3. Where did you mark them? I _____

_____

4. What are you doing now? I'm _____

5. What are you making? I'm _____

6. What will you do after you nail the top to the frame? I'll _____

_____

7. Where are you going to nail the legs? I'm _____

_____

8. Is it going to be a nice table? _____

FUTURE TENSE DICTATION

VERB FORMS

basic forms	make	choose	take	measure	mark	want
past forms	made	chose	took	measured	marked	wanted

	draw	saw	get	nail	pound	turn	cut
	drew	sawed	got	nailed	pounded	turned	cut

PAST TENSE DICTATION

Past Tense: Last Year...

Isaac made this table last year. He chose some nice boards. He measured and marked them. He drew a line where he wanted to cut them. He sawed through each board. He made a frame and nailed the top to it. Then he turned it upside down and nailed the legs to the corners. He's a great carpenter.

---

1. When did Isaac make this table? He _____

_____

2. What did he choose? He _____

3. Where did he draw a line? He _____

_____

4. What did he saw through? He _____

_____

5. What did he nail the top to? He _____

6. What did he nail the legs to? He _____

7. Is he a good carpenter? _____

FOUR TENSES

Complete each question with the correct time phrase. Then give a short answer.

---

soon   recently   often   right now

1. Did he make a table _____recently_____? _No, he didn't._

2. Does he make a table _____? _____

3. Is he making a table _____? _____

4. Will he make a table _____? _____

---

in a few months   every month   a few months ago   at this time

5. Did they choose a pretty table _____? _____

6. Do they choose a pretty table _____? _____

7. Are they choosing a pretty table_____? _____

8. Will they choose a pretty table _____? _____

---

before class today   after class today   in class at this moment   during every class

9. Did you draw a picture _____? _____

10. Do you draw a picture _____? _____

11. Are you drawing a picture _____? _____

12. Will you draw a picture _____? _____

RHYMES

On page 99, find a word that rhymes with:

1. name _____   8. rice _____

2. stop _____   9. park _____

3. Ford _____   10. fine _____

4. mail _____   11. late _____

5. news _____   12. learn _____

6. cable _____   13. pleasure _____

7. blue _____

Find two words that rhyme with:

14. law _____   _____

15. cake _____   _____

Crossword Puzzle

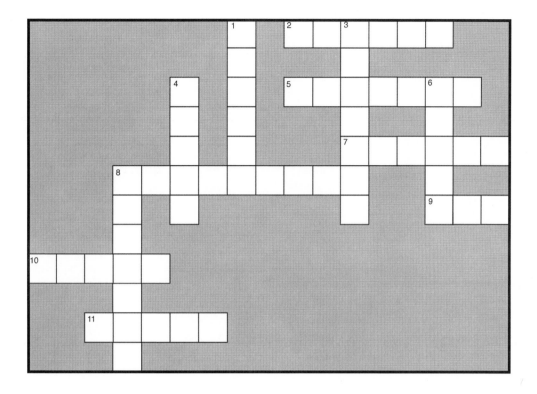

ACROSS

2. Hit the nails with a _____ .
5. a picture made with a pen or pencil
7. Turn it _____ down.
8. a person who builds things
   from wood
9. cut OR past form of see
10. hit hard OR 16 ounces
11. base

DOWN

1. select
3. How long is the board? Use the
   tape _____ .
4. a flat piece of wood
6. small metal connections OR the
   ends of your fingers
8. The table has four _____ .

UNIT 11   OFFICE WORKER

 1. Sit at your desk.

 8. Uh-oh. Here comes the boss.

 2. Relax.

 9. Button your collar.

 3. Take off your jacket.

 10. Tighten your tie.

 4. Loosen your tie.

 11. Put on your jacket.

 5. Unbutton your collar.

 12. Tie your shoes.

 6. Roll up your sleeves.

 13. Get to work.

 7. Untie your shoes.

 14. Say hello to the boss.

WORD STUDY

Match the *opposites*:

_____ 1. relax   a. tighten

_____ 2. loosen   b. roll down

_____ 3. unbutton it   c. put it on

_____ 4. take it off   d. tie

_____ 5. roll up   e. get to work

_d_ 6. untie   f. button it

Match the words that are *similar*:

_____ 1. relax   a. open the buttons

_d_ 2. loosen   b. open your shoes

_____ 3. unbutton   c. make it tight

_____ 4. untie your shoes   d. make it loose

_____ 5. tighten   e. close your shoes

_____ 6. tie you shoes   f. close your buttons

_____ 7. button it   g. take it easy

_____ 8. get to work   h. begin working

Write the plural forms of these nouns:

1. desk   _____   5. boss   _____

2. jacket   _____   6. office   _____

3. sleeve   _____   7. collar   _____

4. shoe   _____

Now practice the pronunciation with your teacher.

REVIEW OF OPPOSITES

You don't like what your friend is doing. Tell your friend to stop. Then say what you want your friend to do. **For example: Don't roll up your sleeves. Roll them down!**

Look below to find the correct sentence to follow each negative sentence and copy it on the same line:

1. Don't relax.   *Get To work!*

2. Don't button your collar.   _____

3. Don't loosen your tie.   _____

4. Don't hang up the phone.   _____

5. Don't tie the hook below the weight.   _____

6. Don't choose an ugly card.   _____

7. Don't sign your name at the top of your note. _____

8. Don't go straight ahead.   _____

9. Don't go faster.   _____

10. Don't turn left.   _____

11. Don't take the tape out.   _____

12. Don't turn off the radio.   _____

13. Don't fast-forward the cassette.   _____

14. Don't take out all the cleaning stuff.   _____

15. Don't fill the wastebaskets.   _____

16. Don't go to sleep.   _____

a. Tighten it!   b. Turn right!   c. Turn around!   d. Turn it on!

e. Wake up!   f. Rewind it!   g. Slow down!   h. Unbutton it!

i. Sign it at the bottom!   j. Choose a pretty one!   k. Get to work!   l. Put it away!

m. Stick it in!   n. Pick up the receiver!   o. Empty them!   p. Tie it above the weight!

PRESENT PROGRESSIVE, LONG ANSWERS

Complete the answers:

1. What is he doing?

He's _____ at

_____ desk.

2. What are they doing?

They're _____ off

_____ jackets.

3. What am I doing?

You're _____

_____ tie.

4. What is she doing?

She's _____ up

_____ sleeves.

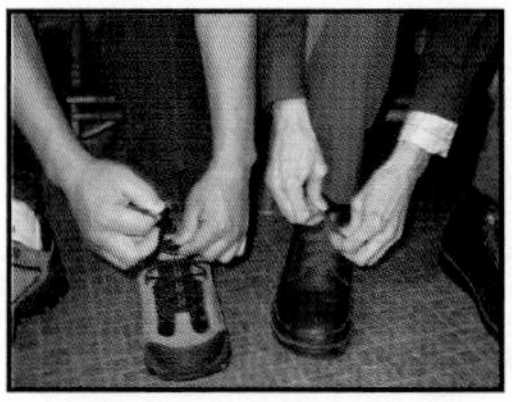

5. What are we doing?

We're _____

_____ shoes.

6. What are you doing?

I'm _____

_____ tie.

7. What is she doing?

She's _____ on

_____ jacket.

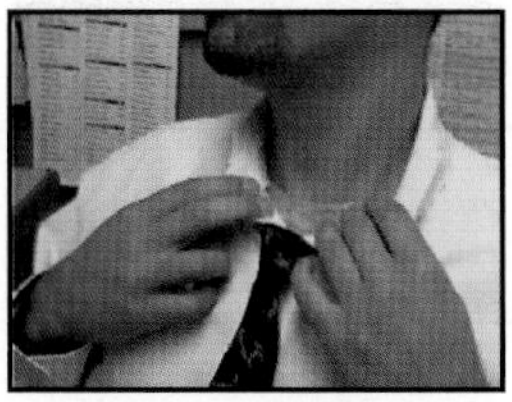

8. What am I doing?

_____

_____

9. What is he doing?

_____

_____

> ### Past, Present Progressive, Future
> Right now Max is relaxing at his desk. A few minutes ago he took off his jacket and loosened his tie. Now he's rolling up his sleeves and untying his shoes. But now he's tightening his tie because the boss is coming! In a minute he'll put on his jacket, tie his shoes, and get to work. Then he'll say hello to the boss.

1. What is Max doing right now? He _____

2. When did he take off his jacket? He _____

_____

3. What did he loosen? He _____

4. What is he rolling up now? He _____

5. What is he untying? He _____

6. Why is he tightening his tie now? He _____

   because _____

7. What will he put on? He _____

   and _____

8. What will he say to the boss? He _____

FUTURE TENSE DICTATION

VERB FORMS

basic forms	sit	relax	take off	loosen	(un)button	roll up
past forms	sat	relaxed	took off	loosened	(un)buttoned	rolled up

come	(un)tie	tighten	put on	get	say
came	(un)tied	tightened	put on	got	said

PAST TENSE DICTATION

Past Tense: This afternoon...

This afternoon Max sat at his desk and relaxed. He took off his jacket, loosened his tie, and unbuttoned his collar. Then he rolled up his sleeves and untied his shoes. But then the boss came! Max buttoned his shirt, tightened his tie and put on his jacket. Then he tied his shoes and got to work. He said hello to the boss.

---

1. Where did Max sit this afternoon? He _____

2. What did he take off? He _____

3. What did he unbutton? He _____

4. What did he roll up? He _____

5. What did he untie? He _____

6. Why did he get to work? He _____

    because _____

7. What did he tighten? He _____

8. What did he say to the boss? He _____

Crossword Puzzle

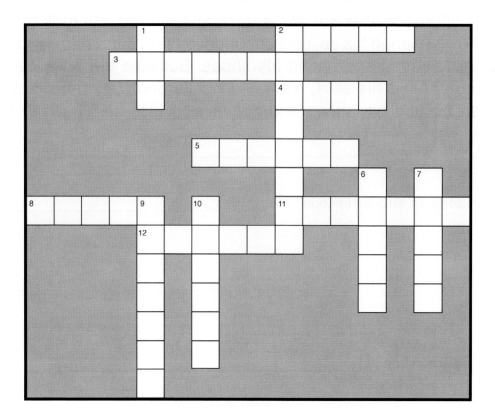

ACROSS

2. open your shoes
3. make it tight
4. employer
5. close the buttons
8. more than one desk
11. more than one office
12. make it loose

DOWN

1. close your shoes
2. open the buttons
6. opposite of loose
7. take it easy
9. the part of the shirt that covers your arms
10. the part of the shirt that goes around your neck

BINGO!

UNIT 12   SOUP FOR LUNCH

1. Pick up the can opener.

2. Open the can.

3. Pour the soup into the pan.

4. Add one can of water.

5. Stir it up.

6. Put it on the stove.

7. Cover it.

8. Turn on the stove.

9. Wait for the soup to heat up.

10. Take off the lid and check it.

11. It's ready. Turn off the heat.

12. Pour some soup into your bowl.

13. Take a sip.

14. Ah! Perfect.

PRESENT PROGRESSIVE
DON'T!

Example: Pick up the can opener.

Don't *pick* up your pencil!

I'm not *picking* up my pencil.

What are you *picking* up?

I'm *picking* up the can opener.

1.   Open the can.

Don't _____ your mouth.

I'm not _____ my mouth.

What are you _____ ?

I'm _____ the can.

2.   Pour the soup into a pan.

Don't _____ the soup into the stove!

I'm not _____ the soup into the stove.

Where are you _____ it?

I'm _____ it into a pan.

3.   Add one can of water.

_____ _____ three cans of water!

I'm _____ _____ three cans of water.

How much water are you _____ ?

I'm _____ one can of water.

4.   Stir it up.

   _____ _____ it with your fingers!

   I'm _____ _____ it with my fingers.

   What _____ _____ it with?

   _____ _____ it with a spoon.

5.   Put it on the stove.

   _____ _____ it on the table!

   _____ _____ _____ it on the table.

   Where _____ _____ _____ it?

   _____ .

6.   Turn on the stove.

   _____ _____ on the TV!

   _____ .

   _____ ?

   _____ .

7.   Wait for the soup to heat up.

   _____ _____ for the bus!

   _____ .

   _____ ?

   _____ .

8.   Take off the lid.

   _____ _____ off your sweater!

   _____ .

   _____ ?

   _____ .

> ## Past, Present Progressive, Future
> It's 12:30 and I'm heating up some soup. At 12:25 I poured the soup into a pan. I added some water and put it on the stove. Now I'm waiting for it. OK, I'm taking off the lid and checking it. In a minute I'm going to turn off the heat. Then I'll pour some soup into my bowl and take a sip.

1. What am I doing right now? You _____

2. When did I pour the soup into a pan? You _____

_____ at _____

3. What did I add? You _____

4. Where did I put it? You _____

5. What am I waiting for? You _____

6. Why am I taking off the lid? You _____ to check it.

7. What am I going to do in a minute? You _____

8. Where will I pour the soup? You _____

PRESENT TENSE CONVERSATION

1. What do you usually eat for lunch? _____

_____

2. Do you ever eat soup for lunch? _____

3. What kind of soup do you like? _____

4. Do you ever heat soup from a can? _____

5. Do you ever cook fresh soup? _____

6. What kind of soup do you cook? _____

7. What **ingredients** do you need to cook soup? _____

_____

8. What do you have to do to cook soup? _____

_____

_____

_____

9. How long do you have to cook soup? _____

10. If you have a favorite recipe for something else, write it here: _____

_____

_____

FUTURE TENSE DICTATION

VERB FORMS

basic form	pick	open	pour	add	stir	put
past forms	picked	opened	poured	added	stirred	put

	cover	turn	wait	heat	take	check
	covered	turned	waited	heated	took	checked

PAST TENSE DICTATION

Past Tense: Yesterday...

Yesterday I heated up some soup. I opened a can and poured the soup into a pan. I added a can of water and stirred it up. I put it on the stove, covered it, and turned on the stove. I waited 15 minutes. Then I took off the lid and checked it. It was ready! I poured some soup into my bowl and took a sip.

---

1. When did I heat up some soup? You _____

2. Where did I pour the soup? You _____

3. How much water did I add? You _____

4. What did I do then? You _____

5. What did I do after I put it on the stove? You _____

_____

6. How long did I wait? You _____

7. How did I check it? You _____

8. Was it ready? _____

9. What did I do after I poured the soup into my bowl? You _____

_____

_____

_____

FOUR TENSES

Complete each question with the correct time phrase. Then give a short answer.

---

at this moment   in a few minutes   a few minutes ago   every time

1. Did he add a can of water _a few minutes ago_ ?   _No, he didn't._

2. Does he add a can of water _____ ? _____

3. Is he adding a can of water _____ ? _____

4. Will he add a can of water _____ ? _____

---

later today   yesterday   right now   every day

5. Did they heat up some soup _____ ? _____

6. Do they heat up some soup _____ ? _____

7. Are they heating up some soup _____ ? _____

8. Are they going to heat up some soup _____ ? _____

---

in a little while   now   whenever she's hungry   a little while ago

9. Did she pour some soup into her bowl _____ ? _____

10. Does she pour some soup into her bowl _____ ? _____

11. Is she pouring some soup into her bowl _____ ? _____

12. Is she going to pour some into her bowl _____ ? _____

Crossword Puzzle

ACROSS

2. top of a pan
3. take a _____ (little liquid into the mouth)
5. opposite of on
6. move food in the pan with a spoon
7. get hot
11. dish for soup or ice cream
12. tool to open a can
13. exactly right

DOWN

1. put in more
2. meal at noon
4. transfer liquid into another dish
6. large appliance for cooking
8. hot liquid food for lunch
9. put the top on
10. finished

r/t Bingo

1.	I want you to meet **Barry**, my	brother.
2.	I want you to meet **Betty**, my	sister.
3.	Can you **hear it**	outside?
4.	Can you **heat it**	on the stove?
5.	I can see her **earring**	under the chair.
6.	I can see her **eating**	her lunch.
7.	**Where** are you	going?
8.	**What** are you	doing?
9.	Where is it?	Here it is!
10.	What is it?	It's a flower.
11.	He's **pouring** the soup	in the bowl.
12.	He's **putting** the soup	on the table.
13.	What is he **wearing**	today?
14.	What is he **waiting**	for?
15.	You're supposed to spell **Carrie** with	double **r**.
16.	You're supposed to spell **Katie** with	a **t**.

Teacher:
Be sure to
download the
FREE
**Teacher's Resource
Guide**

Both you and your students will love the results if you use it in every class session.

See the note to the teacher on page *iii*.

Teacher:
Don't fail to
download the
FREE
**Teacher's Resource
Guide**

It will make a real differ-
ence in the effective-
ness of this workbook.
See the note to the
teacher on page *iii*.

Teacher:
Make sure you download the
FREE
Teacher's Resource Guide

If you use it regularly, you will have lively classes and get even better results.

See the note to the teacher on page *iii*.

DISTRIBUTORS
of Command Performance Language Institute Products

Sky Oaks Productions
P.O. Box 1102
Los Gatos, CA 95031
(408) 395-7600
Fax (408) 395-8440
TPRWorld@aol.com
www.tpr-world.com

Miller Educational Materials
P.O. Box 2428
Buena Park, CA 90621
(800) MEM 4 ESL
Free Fax (888) 462-0042
MillerEdu@aol.com
www.millereducational.com

Canadian Resources for ESL
15 Ravina Crescent
Toronto, Ontario
CANADA M4J 3L9
(416) 466-7875
Fax (416) 466-4383
thane.ladner@sympatico.ca
www.eslresources.com

Multi-Cultural Books & Videos
29280 Bermuda Lane.
Southfield, MI 48076
(248) 948-9999
(800) 567-2220
Fax (248) 948-0030
service@multiculbv.com
www.multiculbv.com

Applause Learning Resources
85 Fernwood Lane
Roslyn, NY 11576-1431
(516) 365-1259
(800) APPLAUSE
Toll Free Fax
    (877) 365-7484
applauselearning@aol.com
www.applauselearning.com

Independent Publishers
    International (IPI)
Sunbridge Bldg. 2F
1-26-6 Yanagibashi,
Taito-ku, Tokyo,
JAPAN 111-0052
Tel: +81-(0)3-5825-3490
Fax: +81-(0)3-5825-3491
contact@indepub.com
www.indepub.com

Calliope Books
Route 3, Box 3395
Saylorsburg, PA 18353
Tel/Fax (610) 381-2587

Berty Segal, Inc.
1749 E. Eucalyptus St.
Brea, CA 92821
(714) 529-5359
Fax (714) 529-3882
bertytprsource@earthlink.net
www.tprsource.com

Entry Publishing & Consulting
P.O. Box 20277
New York, NY 10025
(212) 662-9703
Toll Free (888) 601-9860
Fax: (212) 662-0549
lyngla@earthlink.net

Sosnowski Language Resources
13774 Drake Ct.
Pine, CO 80470
(303) 838-0921
(800) 437-7161
Fax (303) 816-0634
orders@SosnowskiBooks.com
www.sosnowskibooks.com

International Book Centre
2391 Auburn Rd.
Shelby Township, MI 48317
(810) 879-8436
Fax (810) 254-7230
ibcbooks@ibcbooks.com
www.ibcbooks.com

Edumate
2231 Morena Blvd.
San Diego, CA 92110
(619) 275-7117
Fax (619) 275-7120
edumate@aol.com

SpeakWare
2836 Stephen Dr.
Richmond, CA 94803
(510) 222-2455
leds@speakware.com
www.speakware.com

Authors & Editors
10736 Jefferson Blvd. #104
Culver City, CA 90230
(310) 836-2014
authedit@mediaone.net

Continental Book Co.
625 E. 70th Ave., Unit 5
Denver, CO 80229
(303) 289-1761
Fax (800) 279-1764
cbc@continentalbook.com
www.continentalbook.com

Alta Book Center
14 Adrian Court
Burlingame, CA 94010
(650) 692-1285
(800) ALTAESL
Fax (650) 692-4654
Fax (800) ALTAFAX
info@altaesl.com
www.altaesl.com

Midwest European Publications
8124 North Ridgeway Ave.
Skokie, IL 60076
(847) 676-1596
Fax (800) 380-8919
Fax (847) 676-1195
info@mep-eli.com
www.mep-eli.com

BookLink
465 Broad Ave.
Leonia, NJ 07605
(201) 947-3471
Fax (201) 947-6321
booklink@intac.com
www.intac.com/~booklink

Carlex
P.O. Box 81786
Rochester, MI 48308-1786
(800) 526-3768
Fax (248) 852-7142
www.carlexonline.com

Continental Book Co.
80-00 Cooper Ave. #29
Glendale, NY 11385
(718) 326-0560
Fax (718) 326-4276
www.continentalbook.com

David English House
6F Seojung Bldg.
1308-14 Seocho 4 Dong
Seocho-dong
Seoul 137-074
KOREA
Tel (02)594-7625
Fax (02)591-7626
hkhwang1@chollian.net
www.eltkorea.co.kr

Tempo Bookstore
4905 Wisconsin Ave., N.W.
Washington, DC 20016
(202) 363-6683
Fax (202) 363-6686
Tempobookstore@usa.net

Delta Systems, Inc.
1400 Miller Parkway
McHenry, IL 60050
(815) 36-DELTA
(800) 323-8270
Fax (800) 909-9901
custsvc@delta-systems.com
www.delta-systems.com

Multi-Cultural Books & Videos
1594 Caille Avenue.
Belle River, ON-N0R 1A0
CANADA N8N 3V6
(519) 727-4155
Fax (519) 727-4199
service@multiculbv.com
www.multiculbv.com

European Book Co.
925 Larkin St.
San Francisco, CA 94109
(415) 474-0626
Toll Free (877) 746-3666
info@europeanbook.com
www.europeanbook.com

Clarity Language Consultants Ltd.
(Hong Kong and UK)
PO Box 163, Sai Kung,
HONG KONG
Tel (+852) 2791 1787
Fax (+852) 2791 6484
www.clarity.com.hk

World of Reading, Ltd.
P.O. Box 13092
Atlanta, GA 30324-0092
(404) 233-4042
(800) 729-3703
Fax (404) 237-5511
polyglot@wor.com
www.wor.com

Secondary Teachers' Store
3519 E. Ten Mile Rd.
Warren, MI 48091
(800) 783-5174
(586)756-1837
Fax (586)756-2016
www.marygibsonssecondary
    teachersstore.com

Teacher's Discovery
2741 Paldan Dr.
Auburn Hills, MI 48326
(800) TEACHER
(248) 340-7210
Fax (248) 340-7212
www.teachersdiscovery.com

interchange

THIRD EDITION

Jack C. Richards

Intro

STUDENT'S BOOK

CAMBRIDGE UNIVERSITY PRESS
Cambridge, New York, Melbourne, Madrid, Cape Town, Singapore, São Paulo

Cambridge University Press
40 West 20th Street, New York, NY 10011–4211, USA

www.cambridge.org
Information on this title:www.cambridge.org/9780521601498

First published 2005
6th printing 2005
Interchange Third Edition Intro Student's Book has been developed from *New Interchange* Intro Student's Book,
first published by Cambridge University Press in 2000.

Printed in Hong Kong, China

A catalog record for this publication is available from the British Library

ISBN-13   978-0-521-60149-8 Student's Book
ISBN-10   0-521-60149-5 Student's Book

Art direction, book design, photo research, and layout services: Adventure House, NYC
Audio production: Richard LePage & Associates

To the student

Welcome to **Interchange Third Edition**! This revised edition of **New Interchange** gives you many more opportunities to learn and practice English. I am confident this book will help you improve your English! The course combines topics, functions, and grammar. You will learn the four skills of listening, speaking, reading, and writing, in addition to vocabulary and pronunciation.

Each book has 16 units divided into sections, and each section has its own purpose. The **Snapshot** usually introduces the unit's topic with real-world information. The **Word Power** presents new vocabulary. The **Conversation** is a natural, fun dialog that introduces new grammar. You then see and practice this language in the **Grammar Focus**. The **Pronunciation** exercises help you sound like a native speaker.

In the **Listening** section you hear people speaking in many different contexts. You talk in pairs, in groups, or as a class with the many **Speaking** activities. In the **Interchange activities** you talk even more freely about yourself. These fun activities let you share your own ideas and opinions. Finally, at the end of each unit, you read about and further discuss the unit's topic in the **Reading** section.

Frequent **Progress checks** let you check your own development. In these self-assessment exercises *you* decide what material you need to review.

The **Self-study Audio CD** contains the conversations from the unit for extra listening practice. Your CD also has a section with new, original audio material. You can use this in class, in a lab, or at home with the Self-study exercises at the back of this book.

I think you'll enjoy using this book and hope you become better, more confident learners of English. Good luck!

Jack C. Richards

Author's acknowledgments

A great number of people contributed to the development of *Interchange Third Edition*. Particular thanks are owed to the following:

The **reviewers** using *New Interchange* in the following schools and institutes – their insights and suggestions have helped define the content and format of the third edition: Gino Pumadera, **American School**, Guayaquil, Ecuador; Don Ahn, **APEX**, Seoul, Korea; teachers at **AUA Language Center**, Bangkok, Thailand; Linda Martinez, **Canada College**, Redwood City, California, USA; Rosa Maria Valencia Rodriguez, **CEMARC**, Mexico City, Mexico; Wendel Mendes Dantas, **Central Universitária**, São Paulo, Brazil; Lee Altschuler, **Cheng Kung University**, Tainan, Taiwan; Chun Mao Le, **Cheng Siu Institute of Technology**, Kaohsiung, Taiwan; Selma Alfonso, **Colégio Arquidiocesano**, São Paulo, Brazil; Daniel de Mello Ferraz, **Colégio Camargo Aranha**, São Paulo, Brazil; Paula dos Santos Dames, **Colegio Militar do Rio de Janeiro**, Rio de Janeiro, Brazil; Elizabeth Ortiz, **COPOL-COPEI**, Guayaquil, Ecuador; Alexandre de Oliveira, **First Idiomas**, São Paulo, Brazil; João Franco Júnior, **2B Idiomas**, São Paulo, Brazil; Jo Ellen Kaiser and David Martin, **Fort Lauderdale High School**, Fort Lauderdale, Florida, USA; Azusa Okada, **Hiroshima Shudo University**, Hiroshima, Japan; Sandra Herrera and Rosario Valdiria, **INACAP**, Santiago, Chile; Samara Camilo Tome Costa, **Instituto Brasil-Estados Unidos**, Rio de Janeiro, Brazil; Eric Hamilton, **Instituto Chileno Norteamericano de Cultura**, Santiago, Chile; **ICNA**, Santiago, Chile; Pedro Benites, Carolina Chenett, Elena Montero Hurtado, Patricia Nieto, and Antonio Rios, **Instituto Cultural Peruano Norteamericano (ICPNA)**, Lima, Peru; Vanclei Nascimento, **Instituto Pentágono**, São Paulo, Brazil; Michael T. Thornton, **Interactive College of Technology**, Chamblee, Georgia, USA; Norma Aguilera Celis, **IPN ESCA Santo Tomas**, Mexico City, Mexico; Lewis Barksdale, **Kanazawa Institute of Technology**, Ishikawa, Japan; Clare St. Lawrence, Gill Christie, and Sandra Forrester, **Key Language Services**, Quito, Ecuador; Érik Mesquita, **King's Cross**, São Paulo, Brazil; Robert S. Dobie, **Kojen English Language Schools**, Taipei, Taiwan; Shoko Miyagi, **Madison Area Technical College**, Madison, Wisconsin, USA; Atsuko K. Yamazaki, **Institute of Technologists**, Saitama, Japan; teachers and students at **Institute of Technologists**, Saitama, Japan; Gregory Hadley, **Niigata University of International and Information Studies**, Niigata, Japan; Tony Brewer and Frank Claypool, **Osaka College of Foreign Languages and International Business**, Osaka, Japan; Chris Kerr, **Osaka University of Economics and Law**, Osaka, Japan; Angela Suzete Zumpano, **Personal Language Center**, São Paulo, Brazil; Simon Banha Jr. and Tomas S. Martins, **Phil Young's English School**, Curitiba, Brazil; Mehran Sabet and Bob Diem, **Seigakuin University**, Saitama, Japan; Lily Beam, **Shie Jen University**, Kaohsiung, Taiwan; Ray Sullivan, **Shibuya Kyoiku Gakuen Makuhari Senior and Junior High School**, Chiba, Japan; Robert Gee, **Sugiyama Jogakuen University**, Nagoya, Japan; Arthur Tu, **Taipei YMCA**, Taipei, Taiwan; Hiroko Nishikage, Alan Hawk, Peter Riley, and Peter Anyon, **Taisho University**, Tokyo, Japan; Vera Berk, **Talkative Idiomas**, São Paulo, Brazil; Patrick D. McCoy, **Toyo University**, Saitama, Japan; Kathleen Krokar and Ellen D. Sellergren, **Truman College**, Chicago, Illinois, USA; Gabriela Cortes Sanchez, **UAM-A**, Mexico City, Mexico; Marco A. Mora Piedra, **Universidad de Costa Rica**, San Jose, Costa Rica; Janette Carvalhinho de Oliveira, **Universidade Federal do Espirito Santo**, Vitoria, Brazil; Belem Saint Martin Lozada, **Universidad ISEC**, Colegio del Valle, Mexico City, Mexico; Robert Sanchez Flores, **Universidad Nacional Autonoma de Mexico**, Centro de Lenguas Campus Aragon, Mexico City, Mexico; Bertha Chela de Rodriguez, **Universidad Simòn Bolìvar**, Caracas, Venezuela; Marilyn Johnson, **Washoe High School**, Reno, Nevada, USA; Monika Soens, **Yen Ping Senior High School**, Taipei, Taiwan; Kim Yoon Gyong, **Yonsei University**, Seoul, Korea; and Tania Borges Lobao, **York Language Institute**, Rio de Janeiro, Brazil.

The **editorial** and **production** team:
David Bohlke, Jeff Chen, Yuri Hara, Pam Harris, Paul Heacock, Louisa Hellegers, Lise R. Minovitz, Pat Nelson, Bill Paulk, Danielle Power, Mary Sandre, Tami Savir, Kayo Taguchi, Louisa van Houten, Mary Vaughn, Jennifer Wilkin, and Dorothy Zemach.

And Cambridge University Press **staff** and **advisors**:
Jim Anderson, Angela Andrade, Mary Louise Baez, Carlos Barbisan, Kathleen Corley, Kate Cory-Wright, Elizabeth Fuzikava, Steve Golden, Cecilia Gomez, Heather Gray, Bob Hands, Pauline Ireland, Ken Kingery, Gareth Knight, Nigel McQuitty, João Madureira, Andy Martin, Alejandro Martinez, Carine Mitchell, Mark O'Neil, Tom Price, Dan Schulte, Catherine Shih, Howard Siegelman, Ivan Sorrentino, Alcione Tavares, Koen Van Landeghem, and Ellen Zlotnick.

CLASSROOM LANGUAGE Teacher instructions

Plan of Intro Book

Pronunciation/Listening	Writing/Reading	Interchange Activity
Linked sounds Listening for the spelling of names and phone numbers *Self-study*: Listening for personal information	Writing a list of names and phone numbers.	"Famous classmates": Introducing yourself to new people
Plural *-s* endings Listening for the locations of objects *Self-study*: Listening to a conversation about lost things	Writing the locations of objects	"Find the differences": Comparing two pictures of a room
Syllable stress Listening for countries, cities, and languages; listening to descriptions of people *Self-study*: Listening to descriptions of four people	Writing questions requesting personal information	"Board game": Finding out more about your classmates
The letters *s* and *sh* Listening for descriptions of clothing and colors *Self-study*: Listening to a fashion show	Writing questions about what people are wearing	"Celebrity fashions": Describing celebrities' clothing
Rising and falling intonation Listening for times of the day; listening to identify people's actions *Self-study*: Listening to a television show	Writing times of the day "Friends Across a Continent": Reading an online chat between two friends	"What's wrong with this picture": Describing what's wrong with a picture
Third-person singular *-s* endings Listening for activities and days of the week *Self-study*: Listening to questions about your weekly routine	Writing about you and your family "What's Your Schedule Like?": Reading about three people's daily schedules	"Class survey": Finding out more about classmates' habits and routines
Words with *th* Listening to descriptions of homes; listening to people shop for furniture *Self-study*: Listening to a conversation about a new apartment	Writing about your dream home "Two Special Houses in the Southwest": Reading about unusual homes	"Find the differences": Comparing two apartments
Reduction of *do* and *does* Listening to people describe their jobs *Self-study*: Listening to a conversation about a new job	Writing about jobs "Job Profiles": Reading about four unusual jobs	"The perfect job": Figuring out what job is right for you

Titles/Topics	Speaking	Grammar

Pronunciation/Listening	Writing/Reading	Interchange Activity
Sentence stress Listening for people's food preferences *Self-study*: Listening to people discuss foods for a party	Writing questions about mealtime habits "Eating for Good Luck": Reading about foods people eat for good luck in the new year	"Food survey": Taking a survey about foods you eat and comparing answers
Pronunciation of *can* and *can't* Listening for people's favorite sports to watch or play; listening to people talk about their abilities *Self-study*: Listening to people discuss sports and activities	Writing questions about sports "Race the U.S.!": Reading about four unusual races in the U.S.	"Hidden talents": Finding out more about your classmates' hidden talents
Reduction of *going to* Listening to people talk about their evening plans *Self-study*: Listening to a conversation about summer events	Writing about weekend plans "What are you going to do on your birthday?": Reading about birthday customs in different places	"Guessing game": Making guesses about a classmate's plans
Sentence intonation Listening to people talk about health problems; listening for medications *Self-study*: Listening to sentences and questions about health	Writing advice for health problems "10 Simple Ways to Improve Your Health": Reading about ways to improve your health	"Helpful advice": Giving advice for some common problems
Compound nouns Listening to people talk about shopping; listening to directions *Self-study*: Listening to people ask for directions	Writing directions "A Walk Up Fifth Avenue": Reading about popular tourist attractions in New York City	"Giving directions": Asking for directions in a neighborhood
Simple past *-ed* endings Listening to people talk about their past summer activities *Self-study*: Listening to conversations about last weekend	Writing about last weekend "Weekend Stories": Reading about three people's weekend experiences	"Past and present": Comparing your classmates' present lives with their childhoods
Negative contractions Listening for places and dates of birth *Self-study*: Listening to an interview with an actress	Writing questions about a famous person's life "Ricky Martin": Reading about a famous singer's life	"Life events": Making a time line of important events in your life
Reduction of *want to* and *have to* Listening to phone conversations; listening to answering machine messages *Self-study*: Listening for mistakes in answering machine messages	Writing messages "Miami, Florida: What's on This Saturday?": Reading about shows and events on a Web page	"Let's make a date!": Making plans with your classmates

1 It's nice to meet you.

1 CONVERSATION *I'm Jennifer Miller.*

A ▶ Listen and practice.

Michael: Hi. My name is Michael Ota.
Jennifer: I'm Jennifer Miller.
Michael: It's nice to meet you, Jennifer.
Jennifer: Nice to meet you, too.
Michael: I'm sorry. What's your last
             name again?
Jennifer: It's Miller.

first names	last names
↓	↓
Jennifer	Miller
Michael	Ota

B *Pair work* Introduce yourself
to your partner.

2 SNAPSHOT

▶ Listen and practice.

Popular Names and Nicknames in the U.S.

For males		For females	
Names	**Nicknames**	**Names**	**Nicknames**
Anthony	Tony	Elizabeth	Beth
Christopher	Chris	Jennifer	Jen
Joshua	Josh	Katherine	Kathy
Michael	Mike	Nicole	Nicki
Matthew	Matt	Susan	Sue

Sources: *The Professor's Book of First Names; The Parent Soup Baby Name Finder*

Circle the names you know.
Who are some famous people with these names?
What names are popular in your country?

3 GRAMMAR FOCUS

My, your, his, her ▶

What's **your** name?

My name is Jennifer.

What's **his** name?

His name is Michael.

What's **her** name?

Her name is Nicole.

What**'s** = What **is**

Group work Play "The Name Game." Make a circle.
Learn the names of your classmates.

A: My name is Maria.
B: Her name is Maria. I'm Victor.
C: Her name is Maria. His name is Victor. And I'm Kumiko.

4 THE ALPHABET

A ▶ Listen and practice.

A B C D E F G H I J K L M N O P Q R S T U V W X Y Z
a b c d e f g h i j k l m n o p q r s t u v w x y z

B ▶ *Class activity* Listen and practice. Then practice
with your own names. Make a list of your classmates' names.

A: What's your name?
B: I'm Sarah Conner.
A: Is that S-A-R-A-H?
B: Yes, that's right.
A: How do you spell your last name? C-O-N-N-O-R?
B: No, it's C-O-N-N-E-R.

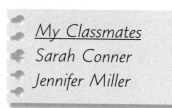

My Classmates
Sarah Conner
Jennifer Miller

5 LISTENING Spelling names

▶ How do you spell the names? Listen and check (✓) the correct answers.

1. ☑ Jon   ☐ John
2. ☐ Sara   ☐ Sarah
3. ☐ Steven   ☐ Stephen
4. ☐ Katherine   ☐ Kathryn
5. ☐ Kris   ☐ Chris

6 WORD POWER Titles

A ▶ Listen and practice.

| **Miss** Ito | (single females) | **Ms.** Chen | (single or married females) |
| **Mrs.** Morgan | (married females) | **Mr.** Garcia | (single or married males) |

B Think of three people. Write their titles and last names.

Miss Lee

7 SAYING HELLO

A ▶ Listen and practice.

B *Class activity* Go around the class. Greet your classmates formally (with titles) and informally (without titles).

8 CONVERSATION *He's over there.*

A  Listen and practice.

Jennifer: Excuse me. Are you
Steven Carson?
David: No, I'm not. He's over there.
Jennifer: Oh, I'm sorry.

Jennifer: Steven? This is your book.
Steven: Oh, it's my math book! Thanks.
You're in my class, right?
Jennifer: Yes, I am. I'm Jennifer Miller.
Steven: It's nice to meet you.

Steven: Hey, David, this is Jennifer.
She's in our math class.
David: Hi, Jennifer.
Jennifer: Hi, David. Nice to meet you.

B *Group work* Greet a classmate. Then introduce him or her to
another classmate.

9 GRAMMAR FOCUS

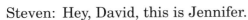

> ### The verb be ▶
>
> **I'm** Jennifer Miller.
> **You're** in my class.
> **She's** in our class. (**Jennifer is** in our class.)
> **He's** over there. (**Steven is** over there.)
> **It's** my math book.
> **It's** Miller. (**My last name is** Miller.)
>
> **Are you** Steven Carson?
> Yes, **I am**.
> No, **I'm not**.
>
> How **are you**?
> **I'm** fine.
>
> *Contractions*
> **I'm** = I am
> **You're** = You are
> **He's** = He is
> **She's** = She is
> **It's** = It is

A Complete the conversation with the correct words in parentheses.
Then practice with a partner.

David: Hello, Jennifer. How ...*are*.... (is / are) you?
Jennifer: .... (She's / I'm) fine, thanks.
.... (I'm / It's) sorry – what's your name again?
David: .... (He's / It's) David – David Medina.
Jennifer: That's right! David, this .... (is / am) Sarah Conner.
.... (She's / He's) in our math class.
David: Hi, Sarah. .... (I'm / It's) nice to meet you.
Sarah: Hi, David. I think .... (you're / I'm) in my English class, too.
David: Oh, right! Yes, I .... (are / am).

B Complete the conversations. Then practice in groups.

Nicole: Excuse me. ...*Are*... you Steven Carson?
David: No, ... not. My name ....
David Medina. Steven .... over there.
Nicole: Oh, sorry.

Nicole: .... you Steven Carson?
Steven: Yes, I ....
Nicole: Hi. .... Nicole Johnson.
Steven: Oh, ... in my math class, right?
Nicole: Yes, I ....
Steven: .... nice to meet you.

C *Class activity* Write your name on a piece of paper. Put the papers in a bag. Then take a different paper. Find the other student.

A: Excuse me. Are you Jin Sook Cho?
B: No, I'm not. He's over there.
A: Hi. Are you Jin Sook Cho?
C: Yes, I am.

10 PRONUNCIATION Linked sounds

 Listen and practice. Notice the linked sounds.

I'm Alan.   You're in our class.   She's over there.

11 NUMBERS

A ▶ Listen and practice.

0	1	2	3	4	5	6	7	8	9	10
zero (oh)	one	two	three	four	five	six	seven	eight	nine	ten

B *Pair work* Practice these numbers.

Name: *Anna Silva*
Work Phone: 201-555-2491
Home Phone: 914-555-2714
Cell Phone: 845-555-1023

Name: *James Liang*
Work Phone: 800-555-8893
Home Phone: 604-555-2714
Cell Phone: 250-555-1023

12 LISTENING Phone numbers

A ▶ Jennifer and Michael are making a list of classmates' phone numbers. Listen and complete the list.

B *Class activity* Make a list of your classmates' names and phone numbers.

A: What's your name?
B: I'm Anna Silva.
A: And what's your phone number?
B: It's (201) 555-2491.

☎

Name	Phone number
David Medina	(212) 555-1937
Sarah Conner	
Steven Carson	
Nicole Johnson	
Jennifer Miller	
Michael Ota	

13 INTERCHANGE 1 Famous classmates

Meet some "famous classmates." Go to Interchange 1 at the back of the book.

14 SAYING GOOD-BYE

A ▶ Listen and practice.

1
See you later, Matthew.
Bye-bye, Lisa.

2
Good-bye. Have a nice day.
See you tomorrow.

3
Bye. Have a good evening.
Thanks, Kim. You, too.

4
Good night, Mrs. Morgan.
Good-bye, Ms. Chen.

B *Class activity* Go around the room. Say good-bye to your classmates and teacher.

2 What's this?

SNAPSHOT

▶ Listen and practice.

What's in your bag?

☐ sunglasses

☐ a hairbrush   ☐ a wallet   ☐ a CD player

■ an address book

☐ a cell phone

☐ keys

☐ a camera

Source: Based on interviews with people between the ages of 16 and 30

Check (✓) the things in your bag.
What other things are in your bag?

ARTICLES *Classroom objects*

A ▶ Listen. Complete these sentences with *a* or *an*.

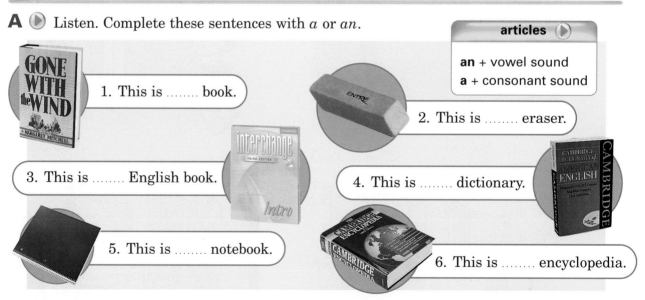

articles ▶
an + vowel sound
a + consonant sound

1. This is .... book.

2. This is .... eraser.

3. This is .... English book.

4. This is .... dictionary.

5. This is .... notebook.

6. This is .... encyclopedia.

B *Pair work* Find and spell these things in your classroom.

board	chair	dictionary	pen	wall
book bag	clock	door	pencil	wastebasket
cassette player	desk	map	table	window

A: This is a board.
B: How do you spell *board*?
A: B-O-A-R-D.

8

③ CONVERSATION They're . . . interesting.

▶ Listen and practice.

Wendy: Wow! What's this?
 Helen: It's a camera.
Wendy: Oh, cool! Thank you, Helen.
       It's great!
 Helen: You're welcome.
   Rex: Now open this box!
Wendy: OK. Uh, what are these?
   Rex: They're earrings.
Wendy: Oh. They're . . . interesting.
       Thank you, Rex. They're
       very nice.

④ PRONUNCIATION Plural -s endings

A ▶ Listen and practice. Notice the pronunciation
of the plural **-s** endings.

s = /z/		s = /s/		(e)s = /ɪz/	
telephone	telephone**s**	desk	desk**s**	sentence	sentence**s**
camera	camera**s**	map	map**s**	exercise	exercise**s**
book bag	book bag**s**	wastebasket	wastebasket**s**	watch	watch**es**

B Say the plural forms of these nouns. Then complete the chart.

address   briefcase   clock   key   newspaper

purse   stamp   television   ticket

/z/	/s/	/ɪz/
		addresses

C ▶ Listen and check your answers.

⑤ GRAMMAR FOCUS

This/these, it/they; *plurals* ▶

This is a camera.

These are cameras.

What's this? It's an earring.

What are these? They're earrings.

Contractions
It's = It is
They're = They are
What's = What is

Complete these conversations. Then practice with a partner.

1. A: What *are these* ?
   B: *They're keys* .

2. A: What *'s this* ?
   B: *It's a CD player* .

3. A: What .... ?
   B: ....

4. A: What .... ?
   B: ....

5. A: What .... ?
   B: ....

6. A: What .... ?
   B: ....

⑥ WHAT'S THIS CALLED?

A ▶ Listen and practice.

A: What's this called in English?
B: I don't know.
C: It's an umbrella.
A: How do you spell that?
C: U-M-B-R-E-L-L-A.

A: What are these called in English?
B: Hmm. I think they're called chopsticks.
A: How do you spell that?
B: C-H-O-P-S-T-I-C-K-S.

B *Group work* Choose four things. Put them on a desk.
Then ask about the name and spelling of each thing.

7 CONVERSATION *Oh, no!*

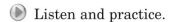 Listen and practice.

Kate: Oh, no! Where are my car keys?
Joe: Relax, Kate. Are they in your purse?
Kate: No, they're not. They're gone!
Joe: I bet they're on the table in the restaurant.
Waiter: Excuse me. Are these your keys?
Kate: Yes, they are. Thank you!
Joe: See? No problem.
Waiter: And is this your wallet?
Kate: Hmm. No, it's not. Where is your wallet, Joe?
Joe: In my pocket. . . . Wait a minute! That *is* my wallet!

8 GRAMMAR FOCUS

> **Yes / No and where questions with be**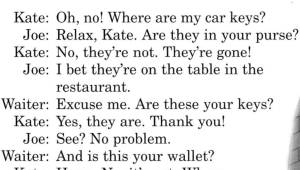
>
> | | |
> |---|---|
> | **Is this** your wallet? | **Where is** your wallet? |
> | Yes, **it is**. / No, **it's not**. | **It's** in my pocket. |
> | **Are these** your keys? | **Where are** my keys? |
> | Yes, **they are**. / No, **they're not**. | **They're** on the table. |

A Complete these conversations. Then practice with a partner.

1. A: ....*Is*.... this your umbrella?
   B: No, ... not.
   A: .... these your keys?
   B: Yes, ... are. Thanks!

2. A: Where .... my glasses?
   B: Are .... your glasses?
   A: No, they're ....
   B: Wait! .... they in your pocket?
   A: Yes, ... are. Thanks!

3. A: Where .... your sunglasses?
   B: .... on the table.
   A: No, ... not. They're *my* sunglasses!
   B: You're right. My sunglasses .... in my purse.

4. A: .... this my pen?
   B: No, ... not. It's *my* pen.
   A: Sorry. .... is my pen?
   B: .... on your desk.
   A: Oh, you're right! .... on my desk.

B *Group work* Put three of your things in a bag. Then choose three different things. Find the owner of each thing.

A: Is this your pen, Yuko?
B: No, it's not.

A: Is this your pen, Sergio?
C: Let me see. Yes, it is.

9 *WORD POWER* *Prepositions; article* the

A ▶ Listen and practice.

Where are **the** keys?
The keys are in **the** box.

in | in front of

behind | on | next to | under

B ▶ Complete these sentences. Then listen and check your answers.

1. The books are *in the book bag* .

2. The DVD player is ....

3. The map is ....

4. The chair is ....

5. The wallet is ....

6. The cell phone is ....

C *Pair work* Ask and answer questions about the pictures in part B.

A: Where are the books?
B: They're in the book bag.

10 *LISTENING* *Kate's things*

▶ Listen. Where are Kate's things? Match the things with their locations.

1. earrings ...*d*...
2. watch ....
3. sunglasses ....
4. address book ....

a. under the table
b. on the chair
c. in front of the television
d. in her purse

11 WHERE ARE JOE'S THINGS?

Pair work Now help Joe find his things. Ask and answer questions.

briefcase	cell phone	newspaper	umbrella
camera	glasses	notebook	wallet

A: Where is his briefcase?
B: It's on the table.

12 INTERCHANGE 2 Find the differences

Compare two pictures of a room. Go to Interchange 2 at the back of the book.

Units 1–2 Progress check

SELF-ASSESSMENT

How well can you do these things? Check (✓) the boxes.

I can	Very well	OK	A little
Introduce myself and another person using statements with *be* (Ex. 1)	☐	☐	☐
Say hello and good-bye (Ex. 1)	☐	☐	☐
Use *my*, *your*, *his*, and *her* (Ex. 1, 2)	☐	☐	☐
Use the alphabet and numbers 0–10 (Ex. 2)	☐	☐	☐
Listen to and understand *this*, *these*, *it*, *they*; articles; and plural *-s* (Ex. 3)	☐	☐	☐
Ask and answer questions about locations using *be* (Ex. 4, 5)	☐	☐	☐

1 HOW ARE YOU?

A Complete the conversation. Use the sentences and questions in the box.

Matt: *Hi. How are you?* ....
Nicki: I'm fine, thanks. ....
Matt: Not bad, thanks. ....
Nicki: And I'm Nicki White.
Matt: ....
Nicki: Nice to meet you, too. ....
Matt: Yes, I am.
Nicki: ....
Matt: See you in class.

> My name is Matt Carlson.
> Oh, are you in my English class?
> How about you?
> ✓ Hi. How are you?
> It's nice to meet you, Nicki.
> Well, have a good day.

B *Pair work* Practice the conversation from part A. Use your own information. Then introduce your partner to a classmate.

"Malena, this is my friend. His name is Tetsu. . . ."

2 IS YOUR PHONE NUMBER . . . ?

Class activity Write your phone number on a piece of paper. Then put the papers in a bag. Take a different paper and find the owner. Write his or her name on the paper.

A: Ali, is your phone number (781) 555-1532?
B: No, it's not. Sorry!
A: Mila, is your . . . ?

14

3 *LISTENING* *What's this? What are these?*

Listen to the conversations. Number the pictures from 1 to 6.

4 WHAT'S WRONG WITH THIS ROOM?

A What's wrong with this room? Make a list.

> The chair is on the desk.

B *Pair work* Ask and answer *Where* questions about the picture.

A: Where's the chair?
B: It's on the desk.

5 YES OR NO GAME

Write five yes/no questions about the picture in Exercise 4. Three have "yes" answers and two have "no" answers. Then ask a partner the questions.

> Is the chair behind the clock?

WHAT'S NEXT?

Look at your Self-assessment again. Do you need to review anything?

3 Where are you from?

SNAPSHOT

▶ Listen and practice.

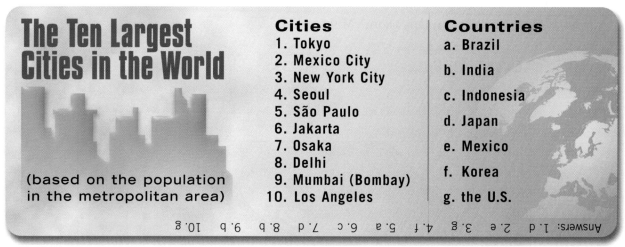

The Ten Largest Cities in the World

(based on the population in the metropolitan area)

Cities
1. Tokyo
2. Mexico City
3. New York City
4. Seoul
5. São Paulo
6. Jakarta
7. Osaka
8. Delhi
9. Mumbai (Bombay)
10. Los Angeles

Countries
a. Brazil
b. India
c. Indonesia
d. Japan
e. Mexico
f. Korea
g. the U.S.

Answers: 1. d   2. e   3. g   4. f   5. a   6. c   7. d   8. b   9. b   10. g

Source: *www.infoplease.com*

Match the cities with the countries. Then check your answers at the bottom of the Snapshot.
What other large cities are in each country? What large cities are in your country?

2 CONVERSATION *Are you from Seoul?*

A ▶ Listen and practice.

Tim: Are you from California, Jessica?
Jessica: Well, my family is in California now, but we're from Korea originally.
Tim: Oh, my mother is Korean – from Seoul! Are you from Seoul?
Jessica: No, we're not from Seoul. We're from Daejeon.
Tim: So is your first language Korean?
Jessica: Yes, it is.

B ▶ Listen to Jessica and Tim talk to Tony, Natasha, and Monique. Check (✓) True or False.

WELCOME NEW STUDENTS

	True	False
1. Tony is from Italy.	☐	☐
2. Natasha is from New York.	☐	☐
3. Monique's first language is English.	☐	☐

16

GRAMMAR FOCUS

Negative statements and yes/no questions with be ▶

I'm not from New York.	**Are you** from California?	**I am.**	**I'm** not.
You're not late.	**Am I** early?	**you are.**	**you're** not.
She's not from Russia.	**Is she** from Brazil?	**she is.**	**she's** not.
He's not from Italy.	**Is he** from Chile?	Yes, **he is.**	No, **he's** not.
It's not English.	**Is it** Korean?	**it is.**	**it's** not.
We're not from Japan.	**Are you** from China?	**we are.**	**we're** not.
You're not early.	**Are we** late?	**you are.**	**you're** not.
They're not in Mexico.	**Are they** in Canada?	**they are.**	**they're** not.

We**'re** = We are

For a list of countries, nationalities, and languages, see the appendix at the back of the book.

A Complete the conversations. Then practice with a partner.

Kyoto, Japan

London, the U.K.

Lima, Peru

1. A: Hiroshi, ...*are*.... you and Maiko from Japan?
   B: Yes, we ....
   A: Oh? .... you from Tokyo?
   B: No, ... not. .... from Kyoto.

2. A: .... Laura from the U.S.?
   B: No, ... not. She's from the U.K.
   A: .... she from London?
   B: Yes, she .... But her parents are from Italy. .... not from the U.K. originally.
   A: .... Laura's first language Italian?
   B: No, ... not. .... English.

3. A: .... Selina and Carlos from Mexico?
   B: No, ... not. .... from Brazil.
   A: .... you from Brazil, too?
   B: No, ... not. I'm from Peru.
   A: So, ... your first language Spanish?
   B: Yes, it ....

B Match the questions with the answers. Then practice with a partner.

1. Are you and your family from Canada? ..*d*..
2. Is your first language English? ......
3. Are you Japanese? ......
4. Is Mr. Ho from Hong Kong? ......
5. Is your mother from the U.S.? ......

a. No, he's not. He's from Singapore.
b. Yes, she is. She's from California.
c. No, it's not. It's Japanese.
d. No, we're not. We're from Australia.
e. Yes, we are. We're from Kyoto.

C Write five questions like the ones in part B. Then ask and answer your questions with a partner.

4 PRONUNCIATION Syllable stress

A ▶ Listen and practice. Notice the syllable stress.

○ ●	● ○	● ○ ○	○ ● ○
China	Japan	Canada	Morocco
Turkey	Brazil	Mexico	Malaysia
....	....	....	....
....	....	....	....

B ▶ What is the syllable stress in these words? Add the words to the chart in part A. Then listen and check.

English	Spanish	Arabic	Korean
Mexican	Honduras	Chinese	Peru

C *Group work* Are the words in part A countries, nationalities, or languages? Make a chart and add more words. Then check your answers in the appendix at the back of the book.

Countries	Nationalities	Languages
China	Chinese	Chinese
Mexico	Mexican	Spanish

5 WHERE ARE THEY FROM?

A Where are these people from? Check (✓) your guesses.

1	2	3	4	5

Thalia	**Charlize Theron**	**Hideo Nomo**	**Celine Dion**	**Tiger Woods**
☐ Brazil	☐ Sweden	☐ Korea	☐ France	☐ the U.S.
☐ Colombia	☐ Ireland	☐ Japan	☐ Canada	☐ England
☐ Mexico	☐ South Africa	☐ China	☐ Australia	☐ New Zealand

B *Group work* Compare your guesses. Then check your answers at the bottom of the page.

A: Is Thalia from Brazil?
B: No, she's not.
C: Is she from Colombia?

6 CONVERSATION *He's cute.*

 Listen and practice.

Emma: Who's that?
  Jill: He's my brother.
Emma: Wow! He's cute. What's his name?
  Jill: James. We call him Jim.
Emma: Oh, how old is he?
  Jill: He's twenty-one years old.
Emma: What's he like? I bet he's nice.
  Jill: Yes, he is – and he's very smart, too!
Emma: And who's that?
  Jill: My sister Tammy. She's only twelve.
       She's the baby of the family.

7 NUMBERS AND AGES

A Listen and practice.

11 eleven	**21** twenty-one	**40** forty
12 twelve	**22** twenty-two	**50** fifty
13 thirteen	**23** twenty-three	**60** sixty
14 fourteen	**24** twenty-four	**70** seventy
15 fifteen	**25** twenty-five	**80** eighty
16 sixteen	**26** twenty-six	**90** ninety
17 seventeen	**27** twenty-seven	**100** one hundred
18 eighteen	**28** twenty-eight	**101** one hundred (and) one
19 nineteen	**29** twenty-nine	**102** one hundred (and) two
20 twenty	**30** thirty	**103** one hundred (and) three

B Listen and practice. Notice the word stress.

thirteen – thirty   fourteen – forty   fifteen – fifty   sixteen – sixty

C *Group work* How old are the people in Exercise 5?
Write down your guesses. Then compare.

A: How old is Thalia?
B: I think she's twenty (years old).
C: Really? I think she's twenty-five.

8 GRAMMAR FOCUS

Wh-questions with be

What's your name?	**Who's that?**	**Who are they?**
My name is Jill.	He's my brother.	They're my classmates.
Where are you from?	**How old is he?**	**Where are they from?**
I'm from Canada.	He's twenty-one.	They're from Rio.
How are you today?	**What's he like?**	**What's Rio like?**
I'm just fine.	He's very nice.	It's very beautiful.
	Who's = Who is	

A Complete the conversations with Wh-questions. Then practice with a partner.

1. A: Look! *Who's that* .... ?
   B: Oh – he's a new student.
   A: .... ?
   B: I think his name is Chien Kuo.
   A: Chien Kuo? .... ?
   B: He's from China.

2. A: Serhat, ... ?
   B: I'm from Turkey – from Istanbul.
   A: .... ?
   B: Istanbul is very old and beautiful.
   A: .... ?
   B: My last name is Erdogan.

3. A: Hi, John. .... ?
   B: I'm just fine. My friend Carolina is here this week – from Argentina.
   A: Carolina? I don't know her.
   .... ?
   B: She's really pretty and very smart.
   A: .... ?
   B: She's eighteen years old.

B *Pair work* Write five Wh-questions about your partner and five Wh-questions about your partner's best friend. Then ask and answer the questions.

Partner	Partner's best friend
Where are you from?	Who's your best friend?

9 INTERCHANGE 3 Board game

Play a board game with your classmates. Go to Interchange 3.

10 WORD POWER Descriptions

A ▶ Listen and practice.

He's really tall.

She's thin.

He's handsome.

She's very pretty.

He's quiet.

She's shy.

He's short.

They're good-looking.

She's talkative.

She's a little heavy.

She's really friendly.

She's serious.

He's funny.

B Complete the chart with words from part A. Add one more word to each list. Then describe your personality and appearance to a partner.

Personality			Appearance		
funny			*handsome*		

"I'm funny, smart, and very handsome."

11 LISTENING Is she very tall?

A ▶ Listen to four descriptions. Check (✓) the correct words.

1. Karen   ✓ short   ☐ tall   3. Elena   ☐ shy   ☐ friendly
2. Marco   ☐ heavy   ☐ thin   4. Andrew   ☐ serious   ☐ funny

B *Group work* Make a list of three people. Then ask and answer questions about the people in your classmates' lists.

A: Who is Eva?
B: She's my friend.
C: How old is she?

Eva
Ramon
Rita

4 I'm not wearing boots!

1 WORD POWER Clothes

A ▶ Listen and practice.

Clothes for Work

shirt
blouse
scarf
tie
belt
skirt
jacket } suit
pants
coat
shoes
(high) heels
raincoat
dress

Clothes for Leisure

hat
cap
T-shirt
sweater
jeans
shorts
gloves
socks
boots
sneakers
pajamas
swimsuits

B Complete the chart with words from part A.

Clothes for warm weather	Clothes for cold weather
....	....
....	....
....	....
....	....

C Circle the clothes in part A you like. Then tell a partner.

"I like the sweater, the gloves, and the boots."

22

② COLORS

A ▶ Listen and practice.

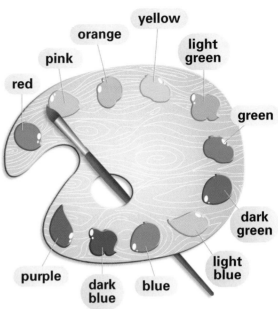

white | light gray | gray
dark gray | beige | light brown
brown | dark brown | black

red, pink, orange, yellow, light green, green, dark green, light blue, blue, dark blue, purple

B *Group work* Ask about favorite colors.

A: What are your favorite colors?
B: My favorite colors are red and purple.

C *Group work* Describe the clothes in Exercise 1.

A: The suit is blue.
B: The pajamas are red and white.

③ CONVERSATION *It's a disaster!*

▶ Listen and practice.

Pat: Great! Our clothes are dry.
 Where is my new blouse?
Julie: What color is it?
Pat: It's white.
Julie: Here's a light blue blouse.
 Is it yours?
Pat: No, it's not mine. . . . Wait.
 It *is* mine. It's a disaster!
Julie: Oh, no! *All* our clothes are
 light blue.
Pat: Here's the problem. It's these
 new blue jeans. Whose jeans
 are they?
Julie: Uh, they're mine. Sorry.

④ PRONUNCIATION *The letters* s *and* sh

A ▶ Listen and practice. Notice the pronunciation of **s** and **sh**.

1. **s**uit   **s**ocks   **sc**arf
2. **sh**irt   **sh**orts   **sh**oes

B Read the sentences. Pay attention to the pronunciation of **s** and **sh**.

1. This is **S**andra's new **sh**irt.
2. These are **S**am's purple **sh**oes!
3. Where are my **sh**oes and **s**ocks?
4. My **sh**orts and T-**sh**irts are blue!

I'm not wearing boots! • 23

GRAMMAR FOCUS

Possessives ▶

Adjectives		Pronouns	Names
my		mine	**Pat's** blouse /s/
your		yours	**Julie's** jeans /z/
These are **his** socks.		his	**Rex's** T-shirt /ɪz/
her	These socks are **hers**.		
our		ours	**Whose** blouse is this? It's **Pat's**.
their		theirs	**Whose** jeans are these? They're **Julie's**.

A Complete the conversations with the correct words in parentheses. Then practice with a partner.

1. A: Is this Jennifer's hat?
   B: No, it's not …*hers*… (her / hers). It's ………… (my / mine).

2. A: Are these ………… (your / yours) gloves?
   B: No, they're not ………… (my / mine) gloves. Let's ask Sally.
   Maybe they're ………… (her / hers) gloves.

3. A: ………… (Whose / Yours) T-shirts are these? Are they Julie's and Pat's?
   B: No, they're not ………… (their / theirs) T-shirts. But these socks are ………… (their / theirs). And these shorts are ………… (your / yours).

4. A: Hey! *These* are not ………… (our / ours) clothes!
   B: You're right. ………… (Our / Ours) are over there.

B *Class activity* Put one of your things in a box. Then choose a different thing from the box. Go around the class and find the owner.

A: Young Min, is this watch yours?
B: No, it's not mine. Maybe it's Rex's.

A: Rex, is this watch yours?
C: No, it's not mine. I think it's Marta's.

6 LISTENING *My T-shirt is yellow.*

A ▶ Listen to these people describe their clothes. Number the pictures from 1 to 4.

B *Pair work* Now talk about these people. What colors are their clothes?

A: What color is Peter's T-shirt?
B: His T-shirt is yellow.

☐ **Bob** ☐ **Elizabeth** ☐ **Diane** 1 **Peter**

7 SNAPSHOT

▶ Listen and practice.

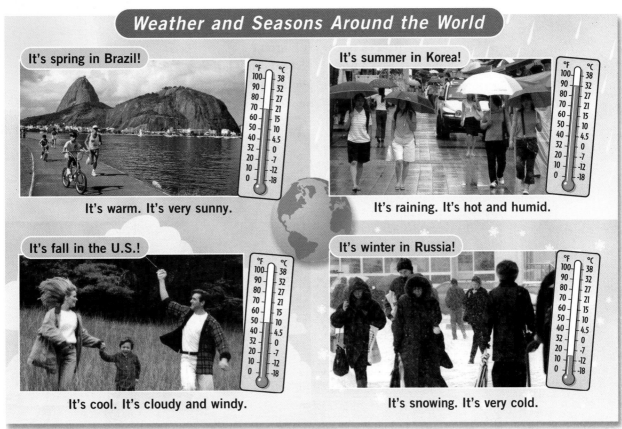

Weather and Seasons Around the World

It's spring in Brazil!

It's warm. It's very sunny.

It's summer in Korea!

It's raining. It's hot and humid.

It's fall in the U.S.!

It's cool. It's cloudy and windy.

It's winter in Russia!

It's snowing. It's very cold.

Source: *Yahoo! Travel*

What are the seasons in your country? Are they like these?
What is your favorite season?
What's the weather like today?

8 CONVERSATION *It's very cold!*

▶ Listen and practice.

Pat: Oh, no!
Julie: What's the matter?
Pat: It's snowing, and it's very cold!
Julie: Are you wearing your gloves?
Pat: No, they're at home.
Julie: Well, you're wearing your coat.
Pat: But my coat isn't warm.
 And I'm not wearing boots!
Julie: OK. Let's take a taxi.
Pat: Thanks, Julie.

Present continuous statements; conjunctions ▶

I'm	I'm not	OR:	**Conjunctions**
You're	You're not	You aren't	It's snowing,
She's wearing shoes.	She's not	She isn't wearing boots.	and it's very cold.
We're	We're not	We aren't	
They're	They're not	They aren't	I'm wearing a coat,
It's snowing.	It's not	It isn't raining.	but I'm not wearing boots.

A Complete these sentences. Then compare with a partner.

1

My name's Claire. I _'m wearing_
a green suit today. I.....................
high heels, too. It's raining, but
I..................... a raincoat.

2

It's hot today. Toshi and Noriko
.... shorts and T-shirts.
It's very sunny, but they ....
sunglasses.

3

Phil .... a suit today –
he .... pants and a jacket.
He .... a brown shirt, but
he .... a tie.

4

It's cold today, but Kathy ....
a coat. She .... a sweatshirt,
gloves, and a hat. She ....
boots. She .... sneakers.

Are you **wearing** a suit?	Yes, I **am**.	No, I'**m not**.
Is she **wearing** boots?	Yes, she **is**.	No, she'**s not** / No, she **isn't**.
Are they **wearing** glasses?	Yes, they **are**.	No, they'**re not** / No, they **aren't**.

B *Pair work* Ask and answer these questions about the pictures in part A.

1. Is Claire wearing a green suit?
2. Is she wearing a raincoat?
3. Is she wearing high heels?
4. Are Toshi and Noriko wearing swimsuits?
5. Are they wearing shorts?
6. Are they wearing sunglasses?

7. Is Phil wearing gray pants?
8. Is he wearing a brown shirt?
9. Is he wearing a tie?
10. Is Kathy wearing boots?
11. Is she wearing a coat?
12. Is she wearing a hat and gloves?

A: Is Claire wearing a green suit?
B: Yes, she is. Is she wearing a raincoat?
A: No, she's not. OR No, she isn't.

C Write four more questions about the pictures in part A. Then ask a partner the questions.

10 LISTENING *He's wearing a T-shirt!*

A ▷ Listen. Write the names **Bruce**, **Beth**, **Jon**, **Anita**, and **Nick** in the correct boxes.

B *Group work* Ask questions about the people in the picture.

A: Is Bruce wearing a light brown jacket?
B: Yes, he is.
C: Is he wearing a tie? . . .

C *Group work* Write five questions about your classmates. Then ask and answer the questions.

Bruce

> Are Sonia and Paulo wearing jeans?
> Is Paulo wearing a red shirt?

11 INTERCHANGE 4 *Celebrity fashions*

What are your favorite celebrities wearing? Go to Interchange 4.

Units 3-4 Progress check

SELF-ASSESSMENT

How well can you do these things? Check (✓) the boxes.

I can	Very well	OK	A little
Ask and answer Wh- and yes/no questions with *be* (Ex. 1)	☐	☐	☐
Talk about countries of origin, nationalities, and languages (Ex. 1)	☐	☐	☐
Listen to, understand, and give descriptions of people (Ex. 2)	☐	☐	☐
Talk about clothes using possessives (Ex. 3)	☐	☐	☐
Compare favorite things using the conjunctions *and* and *but* (Ex. 4)	☐	☐	☐
Talk about clothes using the present continuous (Ex. 5)	☐	☐	☐

1 INTERVIEW

Match the questions with the answers. Then ask and answer the
questions with a partner. Answer with your own information.

1. Are you from Malaysia? ...*h*...
2. Where are you and your family from? ....
3. What is your hometown like? ....
4. Is English your first language? ....
5. Who is your best friend? ....
6. Are your classmates Brazilian? ....
7. How old is your best friend? ....
8. Is our teacher from the U.S.? ....

a. It's very beautiful.
b. Yes, she is.
c. We're from Mexico.
d. My best friend is Kevin.
e. Yes, they are.
f. No, it's not. It's Spanish.
g. He's nineteen.
h. No, I'm not. I'm from Thailand.

2 LISTENING Who's that?

A ▶ Listen to four conversations. Check (✓) the correct description
for each person.

1. Min Ho	☐ tall	☐ short	☐ funny	☐ friendly	☐ talkative	☐ quiet
2. Ryan	☐ tall	☐ short	☐ funny	☐ serious	☐ nice	☐ shy
3. Angela	☐ thin	☐ heavy	☐ pretty	☐ shy	☐ nice	☐ friendly
4. Helen	☐ thin	☐ heavy	☐ quiet	☐ shy	☐ serious	☐ funny

B Write five yes/no questions
about the people in part A.
Then ask a partner the questions.

> *Is Min Ho friendly?*
> *Is Ryan tall?*

28

3 WHOSE CLOTHES ARE THESE?

Class activity Draw three pictures of clothes on different pieces of paper. Then put the papers in a bag. Take three different papers, go around the class, and find the owners.

A: Gina, is this your cap?
B: No, it's not mine. Maybe it's Emi's.

A: Young Woo, are these your pants?
B: Yes, they're mine. Thanks!

4 MY FAVORITE THINGS

A Write your favorite things in the chart. Then ask a partner about his or her favorite things. Write them in the chart.

Favorite	Me	My partner
1. season	....	....
2. color	....	....
3. clothes	....	....

B Compare answers. What's the same? What's different? Write sentences.

Summer is my favorite season, and it's Juan's favorite season, too.
My favorite color is blue, but Juan's favorite color is brown.

5 GUESS THE CLASSMATE

Group work Think of a student in the class. Your classmates ask yes/no questions to guess the student.

A: I'm thinking of a student in this class.
B: Is it a man?
A: Yes, it is.
C: Is he short?
A: No, he isn't.
D: Is he wearing blue jeans? . . .

WHAT'S NEXT?

Look at your Self-assessment again. Do you need to review anything?

5 What are you doing?

① **SNAPSHOT**

▶ Listen and practice.

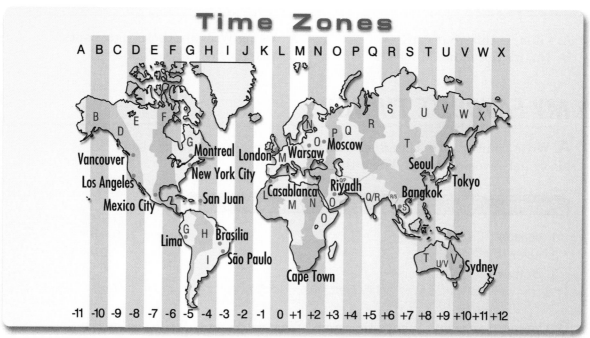

Time Zones

Source: Time Service Department, U.S. Naval Observatory

Which cities are in the same time zones?
Which cities are in your time zone?

② **CONVERSATION** *What time is it there?*

▶ Listen and practice.

Debbie: Hello?
John: Hi, Debbie. This is John.
    I'm calling from Australia.
Debbie: Australia?
John: I'm at a conference in Sydney.
    Remember?
Debbie: Oh, right. What time is it there?
John: It's 10:00 P.M. And it's four o'clock
    there in Los Angeles. Right?
Debbie: Yes – four o'clock in the morning!
John: 4:00 A.M.? Oh, I'm really sorry.
Debbie: That's OK. I'm awake . . . now.

What time is it? ▶

It's one **o'clock**.

It's one-oh-five.
It's five **after** one.

It's one-fifteen.
It's **a quarter after** one.

It's one-thirty.

It's one-forty.
It's twenty **to** two.

It's one forty-five.
It's **a quarter to** two.

A *Pair work* Look at these clocks. What time is it?

1.   2.   3.   4.   5.   6.

A: What time is it?
B: It's twenty after two. OR It's two-twenty.

Is it A.M. **or** P.M.**?** ▶

It's seven (o'clock)
in the morning.
It's 7:00 A.M.

It's twelve (o'clock).
It's 12:00 P.M.
It's **noon**.

It's four (o'clock)
in the afternoon.
It's 4:00 P.M.

It's seven (o'clock)
in the evening.
It's 7:00 P.M.

It's ten (o'clock) **at night**.
It's 10:00 P.M.

It's twelve (o'clock) **at night**.
It's 12:00 A.M.
It's **midnight**.

B *Pair work* Say each time a different way.

1. It's nine o'clock in the evening. *"It's 9:00 P.M."*
2. It's eight o'clock in the morning.
3. It's twelve o'clock at night.
4. It's three in the afternoon.

5. It's 3:00 A.M.
6. It's 6:00 P.M.
7. It's 4:00 P.M.
8. It's 12:00 P.M.

4 LISTENING *It's 4:00 P.M. in Vancouver.*

▶ Tracy and Eric are calling friends in different parts of the world. Listen. What time is it in these cities?

City	Time
Vancouver	*4:00 P.M.*
Bangkok	....
Tokyo	....
São Paulo	....

5 CONVERSATION *I'm really hungry!*

▶ Listen and practice.

Steve: Hi, Mom.
Mom: What are you doing, Steve?
Steve: I'm cooking.
Mom: Why are you cooking now?
It's two o'clock in the morning!
Steve: Well, I'm *really* hungry!
Mom: What are you making?
Steve: Pizza.
Mom: Mmm, pizza. Now I'm getting hungry. Let's eat!

6 PRONUNCIATION *Rising and falling intonation*

A ▶ Listen and practice. Notice the intonation of the yes/no and Wh-questions.

Is she getting up? ↗   What's she doing? ↘
Are they sleeping?   What are they doing?

B ▶ Listen to the questions. Draw a rising arrow (↗) for rising intonation and a falling arrow (↘) for falling intonation.

1. ↗   2. ....   3. ....   4. ....   5. ....   6. ....

Los Angeles   4:00 A.M.

What's Victoria **doing**?
She**'s sleeping** right now.

Mexico City   6:00 A.M.

What's Marcos **doing**?
It's 6:00 A.M., **so he's getting up**.

New York City   7:00 A.M.

What are Sue and Tom **doing**?
They**'re having** breakfast.

Brasília   9:00 A.M.

What's Célia **doing**?
She**'s going** to work.

London   12:00 NOON

What are James and Anne **doing**?
It's noon, **so** they**'re having** lunch.

Moscow   3:00 P.M.

What's Andrei **doing**?
He's working.

Bangkok   7:00 P.M.

What's Permsak **doing**?
He**'s eating** dinner right now.

Tokyo   9:00 P.M.

What's Hiroshi **doing**?
He**'s watching** television.

Your city   00:00

What are you **doing**?
It's . . . , so **I'm** . . .

A *Pair work* Ask and answer the questions about the pictures.

1. **Who**'s sleeping now?
2. **Who**'s having breakfast?
3. **Where**'s Andrei working?
4. **Where**'s Hiroshi watching television?
5. **What**'s Celia wearing?
6. **What**'s Marcos wearing?
7. **Why** is Marcos getting up?
8. **Why** are James and Anne having lunch?

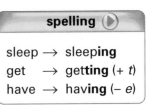

spelling ▶

sleep → slee**ping**
get   → ge**tting** (+ *t*)
have → hav**ing** (– *e*)

B *Group work* Write five more questions about the pictures.
Then ask and answer your questions in groups.

8 WORD POWER Activities

A ▶ Listen and practice. *"He's playing tennis."*

play tennis

ride a bike

run

swim

take a walk

dance

drive

go to the movies

shop

read

study

watch television

B *Group work* Ask and answer questions about the pictures in part A.

A: Is he playing soccer?
B: No, he's not.
C: What's he doing?
A: He's playing tennis.

C *Group work* Act out the verbs and guess the actions.

A: (*acting out dancing*)   C: Are you dancing?
B: Are you swimming?   A: Yes, I am.
A: No, I'm not.

9 LISTENING Mary's activities

A ▶ What's Mary doing? Listen to the sounds and number
the actions from 1 to 8.

☐ dancing	☐ eating dinner	☐ riding a bike	☐ swimming
[1] driving	☐ playing tennis	☐ shopping	☐ watching television

B ▶ *Pair work* Listen again. Ask and answer questions about each sound.

A: What's Mary doing right now?
B: She's driving.

10 INTERCHANGE 5 What's wrong with this picture?

What's wrong with this picture? Go to Interchange 5.

Friends Across a Continent

Skim the conversation. Write the name of the correct person under each picture.

Meg Martin and Kathy O'Brien chat online almost every day. Meg is an exchange student from the U.S. She is studying in Mexico. Kathy is in the U.S.

megm: Hi, there!

kathyo: Hi, Meg!

megm: What are you doing?

kathyo: I'm sitting on my bed with my laptop computer. I'm doing my homework.

megm: What are you working on?

kathyo: I'm writing an essay for Spanish class. : ^)

megm: Can you chat?

kathyo: For a minute. Where are you?

megm: I'm in an Internet café with my friend Carmen. I'm having coffee and she's reading a magazine. How is your family?

kathyo: They're all fine! My father's working outside. He's mowing the lawn. My mother is out shopping.

megm: Where's your brother?

kathyo: John's not home. He's playing soccer in the park. Oh, wait. My mother is home. She's calling me. I have to go!

megm: OK! Bye!

kathyo: Bye! :)

A Read the conversation. Then answer these questions.

Who is . . . ?

1. writing an essay ....
2. having coffee ....
3. reading a magazine ....
4. working outside ....
5. shopping ....
6. playing soccer ....

B *Pair work* Imagine you are having an online chat. Where are you? Who are you chatting with? Write a short conversation.

6 My sister works downtown.

1 SNAPSHOT

▶ Listen and practice.

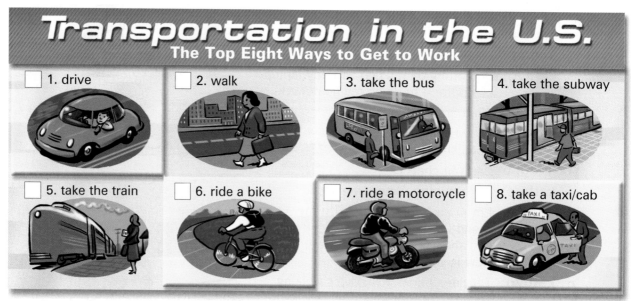

Transportation in the U.S.
The Top Eight Ways to Get to Work

1. drive
2. walk
3. take the bus
4. take the subway
5. take the train
6. ride a bike
7. ride a motorcycle
8. take a taxi/cab

Source: U.S. Census Bureau

Check (✓) the kinds of transportation you use.
What are some other kinds of transportation?

2 CONVERSATION *Nice car!*

▶ Listen and practice.

Ashley: Nice car, Jason! Is it yours?
Jason: No, it's my sister's. She has a new job, and she drives to work.
Ashley: Is her job here in the suburbs?
Jason: No, it's downtown.
Ashley: My parents work downtown, but they don't drive to work. They use public transportation.
Jason: The bus or the train?
Ashley: The train doesn't stop near our house, so they take the bus. It's really slow.
Jason: That's too bad.

③ WORD POWER Family

A *Pair work* Complete the sentences about
the Carter family. Then listen and check your answers.

1. Anne is Paul's ....*wife*.... .
2. Jason and Emily are their ....
3. Paul is Anne's ....
4. Jason is Anne's ....
5. Emily is Paul's ....
6. Jason is Emily's ....
7. Emily is Jason's ....
8. Paul and Anne are
   Jason's ....

kids = children
mom = mother
dad = father

B *Pair work* Tell your partner
about your family.

"My mother's name is Angela.
David and Daniel are my brothers."

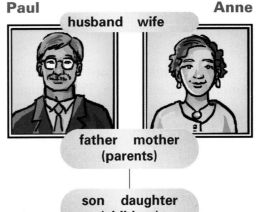

Paul   Anne

husband   wife

father   mother
(parents)

son   daughter
(children)

brother   sister

Jason   Emily

④ GRAMMAR FOCUS

Simple present statements ▶

						Contractions
I	**walk**	to school.	I	**don't live**	far from here.	**don't** = do not
You	**ride**	your bike to school.	You	**don't live**	near here.	**doesn't** = does not
He	**works**	near here.	He	**doesn't work**	downtown.	
She	**takes**	the bus to work.	She	**doesn't drive**	to work.	
We	**live**	with our parents.	We	**don't live**	alone.	
They	**use**	public transportation.	They	**don't need**	a car.	

A Paul Carter is talking about his family. Complete the sentences
with the correct verb forms. Then compare with a partner.

1. My family and I ...*live*... (live / lives) in the suburbs. My wife and I
   .... (work / works) near here, so we .... (walk / walks) to
   work. Our daughter Emily .... (work / works) downtown, so she
   .... (drive / drives) to work. Our son .... (don't / doesn't)
   drive. He .... (ride / rides) his bike to school.

2. My parents .... (live / lives) in the city. My mother
   .... (take / takes) a train to work. My father is retired, so he
   .... (don't / doesn't) work now. He also .... (use / uses)
   public transportation, so they .... (don't / doesn't) need a car.

My sister works downtown. • **37**

> **Simple present statements with irregular verbs** ▶

I/you/we/they	he/she/it
I **have** a bike.	My father **has** a car.
We **do** our homework every day.	My mother **does** a lot of work at home.
My parents **go** to work by bus.	The bus **goes** downtown.

B Ashley is talking about her family and her friend Jason.
Complete the sentences. Then compare with a partner.

1. My parents ..*have*.. (have / has) a house in the suburbs. My mom
   and dad .... (go / goes) downtown to work. My parents are very
   busy, so I .... (do / does) a lot of work at home.

2. My brother doesn't live with us. He .... (have / has) an
   apartment in the city. He .... (go / goes) to school all day, and he
   .... (do / does) office work at night.

3. I .... (have / has) a new friend. His name is Jason. We ....
   (go / goes) to the same school, and sometimes we .... (do / does)
   our homework together.

C *Pair work* Tell your partner about your family.

"I have one brother and two sisters. They . . ."

PRONUNCIATION *Third-person singular -s endings*

▶ Listen and practice. Notice the pronunciation of the **-s** endings.

s = /s/	*s = /z/*	*(e)s = /ɪz/*	*irregular*
take take**s**	go go**es**	dance dance**s**	do does
walk walk**s**	study stud**ies**	watch watch**es**	have has

WHO IS IT?

A Write five sentences about you and your family.
Write "Male" or "Female" on your paper, but not your name.

> *(Female) I live with my parents. I have two*
> *sisters. My father works downtown. . . .*

B *Class activity* Put all the papers in a bag. Choose a paper
and describe the writer. Your classmates guess the writer.

A: She lives with her parents. She has two sisters. Her
   father works downtown. . . . Who is it?
B: Michelle, is it you?
C: No, it's not me. . . .

7 CONVERSATION *I get up at noon.*

 Listen and practice.

Jack: Let's go to the park on Sunday.
Amy: OK, but let's go in the afternoon. I sleep late on weekends.
Jack: What time do you get up on Sundays?
Amy: At ten o'clock.
Jack: Oh, that's early. On Sundays I get up at noon.
Amy: Do you eat breakfast then?
Jack: Sure. I have breakfast every day.
Amy: Then let's meet at this restaurant at one o'clock. They serve breakfast all day!

8 GRAMMAR FOCUS

Simple present questions

Do you **get up** early?
  No, I **get up** late.
Does he **have** lunch at noon?
  No, he **eats** lunch at one o'clock.
Do they **drive** to work?
  Yes, they **drive** to work every day.

What time do you **get up**?
  At ten o'clock.
What time does he **have** lunch?
  At one o'clock.
When do they **drive** to work?
  Every day.

A Complete the questions with *do* or *does*. Then write four more questions.

1. ...*Do*... you get up early on weekdays?
2. What time .... you go home?
3. .... your mother work?
4. How .... your father get to work?
5. .... your parents read in the evening?
6. When .... your parents shop?
7. Does .... ?
8. What time .... ?
9. Do .... ?
10. When .... ?

time expressions	
early	**in** the morning
late	**in** the afternoon
every day	**in** the evening
at 9:00	**on** Sundays
at noon/midnight	**on** weekends
at night	**on** weekdays

B *Pair work* Ask and answer the questions from part A. Use time expressions from the box.

A: Do you get up early on weekdays?
B: Yes, I do. I get up at seven o'clock.

C Unscramble the questions to complete the conversations. Then ask a partner the questions. Answer with your own information.

1. A: *Do you exercise every day* ?
       (you   every day   exercise   do)
    B: Yes, I exercise every day.

2. A: .... ?
       (you   what time   lunch   do   eat)
    B: At 1:00 P.M.

3. A: .... ?
       (at   start   does   eight o'clock   this class)
    B: No, this class starts at nine o'clock.

4. A: .... ?
       (study   you   English   do   when)
    B: I study English in the evening.

 9 ## LISTENING *Marsha's weekly routine*

A  Listen to Marsha talk about her weekly routine.
Check (✓) the days she does each thing.

	Monday	**Tuesday**	**Wednesday**	**Thursday**	**Friday**	**Saturday**	**Sunday**
get up early	☐	☐	☐	☐	☐	☐	☐
go to work	☐	☐	☐	☐	☐	☐	☐
exercise	☐	☐	☐	☐	☐	☐	☐
see friends	☐	☐	☐	☐	☐	☐	☐
see family	☐	☐	☐	☐	☐	☐	☐

B *Group work* Tell your classmates about your weekly routine.

A: I get up early on weekdays and Saturdays.
   But I sleep late on Sundays. . . .
B: I get up early on weekdays, too.
   I get up at 6:00.
C: Really? I get up late every day. . . .

 10 ## INTERCHANGE 6 *Class survey*

Find out more about your classmates. Go to Interchange 6.

What's your schedule like?

Look at the pictures and the labels. Who gets up early? Who gets up late?

Student reporter Mike Starr talks to people on the street about their schedules.

Brittany Davis
College Student

Joshua Burns
Web-site Designer

Maya Black
Rock Musician

Mike: What's your schedule like?

Brittany: My classes start at 8:00 A.M., so I get up at 7:00 and take the bus to school.

MS: When do your classes end?

BD: They end at noon. Then I have a job at the library.

MS: So when do you study?

BD: My only time to study is in the evening, from eight until midnight.

Mike: What's your schedule like?

Joshua: Well, I get up at 6:30 A.M. and go for a run before breakfast.

MS: How do you go to work?

JB: I work at home. I start work at 8:00. Around 1:00, I take a lunch break.

MS: How late do you work?

JB: Sometimes I work all night to finish a project!

Mike: What's your schedule like?

Maya: I work at night. I go to work at 10:00 P.M., and I play until 3:00 A.M.

MS: What do you do after work?

MB: I have dinner. Then I take a taxi home.

MS: What time do you go to bed?

MB: I go to bed at 5:00 in the morning.

A Read the article. Then number the activities in each person's schedule from 1 to 5.

Brittany Davis	**Joshua Burns**	**Maya Black**
.... a. She goes to class.	.... a. He has breakfast.	.... a. She has dinner.
.... b. She takes the bus.	.... b. He starts work.	.... b. She finishes work.
.... c. She works.	.... c. He eats lunch.	.... c. She goes to bed.
.... d. She studies.	.... d. He gets up.	.... d. She goes to work.
...1... e. She gets up.	.... e. He goes for a run.	.... e. She goes home.

B Write five sentences about your schedule. Are you an "early bird" or a "night owl"? Compare with a partner.

early bird

night owl

Units 5–6 Progress check

SELF-ASSESSMENT

How well can you do these things? Check (✓) the boxes.

I can	Very well	OK	A little
Listen to and understand cities, times, and activities (Ex. 1)	☐	☐	☐
Ask and answer questions using the present continuous (Ex. 2)	☐	☐	☐
Talk about weekly routines using simple present statements (Ex. 3)	☐	☐	☐
Ask and answer questions using the simple present (Ex. 4, 5)	☐	☐	☐
Talk about lifestyles and famous people (Ex. 4, 5)	☐	☐	☐

1 LISTENING *Around the world*

▶ It's 9 A.M. in Los Angeles. Victoria is calling friends around the world. Listen to the conversations and complete the chart.

	City	Time	Activity
1. Sue	*New York*	....	....
2. Marcos	....	....	....
3. Jim	....	....	....

2 ON VACATION

Student A: Imagine your classmates are on vacation. Student B calls you. Ask questions about your classmates.

Student B: Imagine you are on vacation with your classmates. Call Student A. Answer Student A's questions about your classmates.

A: Hello?
B: Hi, it's . . . . I'm on vacation in . . .
A: In . . . ? Wow! Who are you with? What are you doing?
B: . . .
A: Well, have fun. Bye!

3 MY WEEKLY ROUTINE

A What do you do on these days? Complete the chart.

On weekdays	
On weekends	
Every day	

B *Pair work* Compare routines. How are they the same? different?

A: I watch television on weekdays.
B: I do, too. I also cook on weekdays.
A: Oh, I don't cook on weekdays. But I cook on weekends!

C *Class activity* Tell the class about your partner's weekly routine.

"Celia doesn't cook on weekdays, but she cooks on weekends. . . ."

4 LIFESTYLE SURVEY

A Answer the questions in the chart. Check (✓) Yes or No.

	Yes	No	Name
1. Do you live with your parents?	☐	☐	....
2. Do both your parents work?	☐	☐	....
3. Do you watch television at night?	☐	☐	....
4. Do you eat dinner with your family?	☐	☐	....
5. Do you stay home on weekends?	☐	☐	....
6. Do you work on Saturdays?	☐	☐	....

B *Class activity* Go around the class and find classmates with the same answers. Write their names in the chart. Try to write a different name on each line.

5 WHO IS IT?

Group work Think of a famous person. Your classmates ask yes/no questions to guess the person.

Is it a man? a woman?
Does he/she live in . . . ?
Is he/she a singer? an actor?

Is he/she tall? short?
Does he/she wear glasses?

WHAT'S NEXT?

Look at your Self-assessment again. Do you need to review anything?

7 Does it have a view?

SNAPSHOT

▶ Listen and practice.

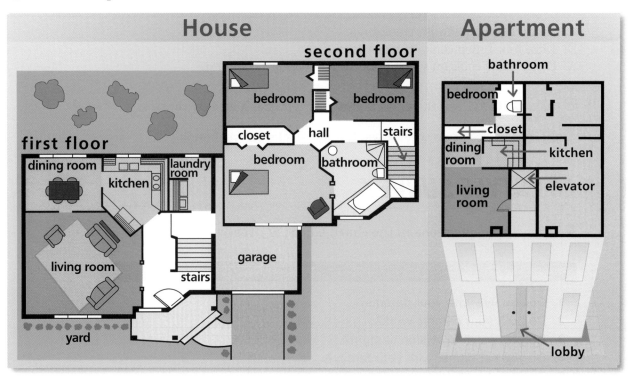

What rooms are in houses in your country? What rooms are in apartments?
What rooms are in your house or apartment?

CONVERSATION *My new apartment*

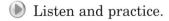 Listen and practice.

Linda: Guess what! I have a new apartment.
Chris: That's great! What's it like?
Linda: It's really beautiful.
Chris: Is it very big?
Linda: Well, it has a big living room, a small bedroom, a bathroom, and a kitchen.
Chris: Where is it?
Linda: On Lakeview Drive.
Chris: Oh, nice! Does it have a view?
Linda: Yes, it does. It has a great view of another apartment building!

44

Simple present short answers ▶

Do you **live** in an apartment? Yes, I **do**. No, I **don't**.	**Does** Chris **live** in a house? Yes, he **does**. No, he **doesn't**.
Do the bedrooms **have** windows? Yes, they **do**. No, they **don't**.	**Does** the house **have** a yard? Yes, it **does**. No, it **doesn't**.

A Complete the conversation. Then practice with a partner.

Linda: ...*Do*... you ...*live*... in an apartment?
Chris: No, I .... I .... in a house.
Linda: .... it .... a yard?
Chris: Yes, it ....
Linda: That sounds nice. .... you .... alone?
Chris: No, I .... I .... with my family.
Linda: .... you .... any brothers or sisters?
Chris: Yes, I .... I .... four sisters.
Linda: That's a big family. .... you .... a big house?
Chris: Yes, we .... It .... ten rooms.
Linda: Ten rooms! .... it .... many bedrooms?
Chris: Yes, it .... It .... four.
Linda: .... you .... your own bedroom?
Chris: Yes, I .... I'm really lucky.

B *Pair work* Read the conversation in part A again. Ask and answer
these questions. For "no" answers, give the correct information.

1. Does Chris live in an apartment?
   "No, he doesn't. He lives in a house."
2. Does Chris's house have a yard?

3. Does Chris live alone?
4. Does he have four brothers?
5. Does he have his own room?

C *Pair work* Write five questions to ask your partner about his or her
home. Then ask and answer the questions.

4 ## LISTENING *It has just one room.*

▶ Listen to four people describe their homes. Number the pictures from 1 to 4.

1

5 WORD POWER Furniture

A ▶ Listen and practice.

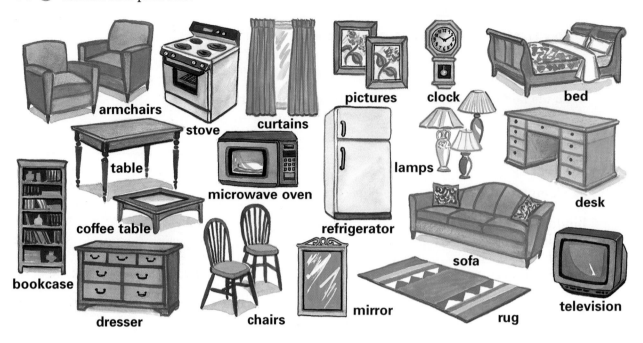

armchairs
stove
curtains
pictures
clock
bed
table
microwave oven
lamps
refrigerator
desk
coffee table
sofa
bookcase
dresser
chairs
mirror
rug
television

B Which rooms have the things in part A? Complete the chart.

Kitchen	table stove
Dining room	table
Living room	
Bedroom	

C *Group work* What furniture do you have? Tell your classmates.

"My living room has a sofa, a rug, and a television. . . ."

6 CONVERSATION There aren't any chairs.

▶ Listen and practice.

Chris: This apartment is great.
Linda: Thanks. I love it, but I really need some furniture.
Chris: What do you need?
Linda: Oh, I need lots of things. There are some chairs in the kitchen, but there isn't a table.
Chris: And there's no sofa here in the living room.
Linda: And there aren't any chairs. There's only this lamp.
Chris: So let's go shopping next weekend!

There is, there are ▶

There's a bed in the bedroom.
There's no sofa in the bedroom.
There isn't a table in the kitchen.

There are some chairs in the kitchen.
There are no chairs in the living room.
There aren't any chairs in the living room.

There's = There is

A Write each sentence a different way. Then practice with a partner.

1. I don't have a table in the bedroom.
2. I have some chairs in the kitchen.
3. I have a stove in the kitchen.
4. I don't have a refrigerator.
5. I don't have curtains on the windows.
6. I don't have any rugs on the floor.

...There's no... table in the bedroom.
.... chairs in the kitchen.
.... stove in the kitchen.
.... a refrigerator.
.... curtains on the windows.
.... rugs on the floor.

B *Pair work* Look at the picture of Linda's apartment. Say what she has and doesn't have.

A: There's a mirror in the bedroom.
B: But there aren't any pictures in the bedroom.

C Write five sentences about things you have or don't have in your classroom. Then compare with a partner.

There are twenty desks in the classroom.
There aren't any computers.

8 **INTERCHANGE 7** *Find the differences*

Compare two apartments. Go to Interchange 7.

9 *PRONUNCIATION* Words with th

A ▶ Listen and practice. Notice the pronunciation of /θ/ and /ð/.

/ð/   /θ/   /ð/   /ð/   /θ/   /θ/
There are **th**irteen rooms in **th**is house. **Th**e house has **th**ree ba**th**rooms.

B *Pair work* List other words with /θ/ and /ð/. Then use them to write four funny sentences. Read them aloud.

> *On Thursdays, their mother and father think for thirteen minutes.*

10 *LISTENING* Furniture is expensive!

▶ Listen to Chris and Linda talk in a furniture store.
What does Linda like? Check (✓) the things.

> ☑ chairs   ☐ a sofa   ☐ a rug   ☐ a table
> ☐ a refrigerator ☐ a dresser ☐ a coffee table ☐ curtains

11 *MY DREAM HOME*

A Write a description of your dream home.

What is your dream home like?
Where is it?
What rooms does it have?
What things are in the rooms?
Does it have a view?

> *My dream home is a cabin*
> *in the forest. There is one*
> *large room. . . .*

penthouse

cabin

houseboat

B *Pair work* Ask your partner about his or her dream home.

A: Does it have a view?
B: Yes, it has a very nice view of the forest. . . .

villa

Two Special Houses in the **American Southwest**

Scan the article. Where is Ms. Cisneros's house? Where is Ms. Nelson's house?

Every year, many people visit Arizona to learn about Native American tribes. Most people stay in hotels, but some people stay in traditional Native American homes, called *hogans*. Lorraine Nelson, a teacher from Arizona, invites visitors to stay in her hogan. It has three chairs, two beds on the floor, and a wood-burning stove. Ms. Nelson teaches her guests about Native American traditions.

In San Antonio, Texas, there is a purple house. This house is the home of Sandra Cisneros. Ms. Cisneros is a Mexican-American writer. She is famous for her interesting stories. The house has a porch with a pink floor. The rooms are green, pink, and purple. There are many books and colorful paintings. Many other houses near Ms. Cisneros's house are white or beige, so her house is very different. Some of her neighbors think her house is too colorful, but Ms. Cisneros loves it.

A Read the article. What's in each house? Complete the chart.

three chairs   colorful paintings   two beds on the floor
many books   ✓ porch with a pink floor   wood-burning stove

Sandra Cisneros's house	Lorraine Nelson's hogan
1. There is a *porch with a pink floor* .	4. There is a ....
2. There are	5. There are ....
3. There are	6. There are ....

B *Group work* Talk about these questions.

1. Imagine you are painting your house. What colors do you use? Why?
2. Imagine you are visiting Arizona. Do you stay in a hogan or in a hotel? Why?

8 What do you do?

① WORD POWER Jobs

A ▶ Match the jobs with the pictures. Then listen and practice. *"He's a receptionist."*

a. cashier	e. judge	i. pilot	m. security guard
b. cook/chef	f. lawyer	j. police officer	n. singer
c. doctor	g. musician	✓k. receptionist	o. waiter
d. flight attendant	h. nurse	l. salesperson	p. waitress

1. k 2. ☐ 3. ☐

4. ☐ 5. ☐

6. ☐ 7. ☐

8. ☐ 9. ☐ 10. ☐

11. ☐ 12. ☐ 13. ☐

14. ☐ 15. ☐ 16. ☐

B *Pair work* Ask questions about the people in part A. What are their jobs?

A: What's his job?
B: He's a receptionist.

2 THE WORKPLACE

A *Pair work* Who works in these places? Complete the chart with jobs from Exercise 1. Add one more job to each list.

A: A doctor works in a hospital.
B: A nurse works in a hospital, too.

In a hospital	In an office	In a store	In a hotel
doctor			
nurse			

B *Class activity* Ask and answer *Who* questions about jobs. Use these words.

wears a uniform	sits all day	talks to people	works hard
stands all day	handles money	works at night	writes tickets

A: Who wears a uniform?
B: A police officer wears a uniform.
C: And a security guard . . .

3 CONVERSATION *He works in a hotel.*

 Listen and practice.

Rachel: Where does your brother work?
Angela: In a hotel.
Rachel: Oh, really? My brother works in a hotel, too. He's a front desk agent.
Angela: How does he like it?
Rachel: Not very much. He doesn't like the manager.
Angela: That's too bad. What hotel does he work for?
Rachel: The Plaza.
Angela: That's funny. My brother works there, too.
Rachel: Oh, that's interesting. What does he do?
Angela: Actually, he's the manager!

4 PRONUNCIATION *Reduction of do and does*

Listen and practice. Notice the reduction of **do** and **does**.

Where **do you** work?   Where **does he** work?   Where **do they** work?

What **do you** do?   What **does he** do?   What **do they** do?

5 GRAMMAR FOCUS

Simple present Wh-questions

Where do you **work?**	**Where does** he **work?**	**Where do** they **work?**
In a hospital.	In a hotel.	In a restaurant.
What do you **do?**	**What does** he **do?**	**What do** they **do?**
I'm a doctor.	He's a manager.	They're waiters.
How do you **like** it?	**How does** he **like** it?	**How do** they **like** it?
I really like it.	It's OK.	They hate it.

A Complete these conversations. Then practice with a partner.

1. A: _What_ does your sister _do_ ?
   B: My sister? She's a nurse.
   A: .... does she .... it?
   B: It's difficult, but she loves it.

2. A: .... does your brother .... ?
   B: At the airport. He's a pilot.
   A: Oh? .... does he .... it?
   B: He doesn't really like it.

3. A: .... do your parents .... their jobs?
   B: Oh, I guess they like them.
   A: I don't remember. .... do they .... ?
   B: In an office in the city.

4. A: .... do you .... ?
   B: I'm a student.
   A: I see. .... do you .... your classes?
   B: They're good. I like them a lot.

B *Pair work* Ask questions about these people. Where do they work?
What do they do? How do they like it?

Ben

Claudia

Vicki and Owen

A: Where does Ben work?
B: He works in . . .

6 SNAPSHOT

▶ Listen and practice.

Job Survey – People's opinions of different jobs

	Exciting	Boring	Easy	Difficult	Safe	Dangerous	Relaxing	Stressful
cashier	☐	☐	✓	☐	☐	☐	☐	☐
chef	☐	☐	☐	☐	☐	☐	☐	✓
flight attendant	☐	☐	☐	✓	☐	☐	☐	☐
judge	☐	☐	☐	☐	☐	☐	☐	✓
musician	☐	☐	☐	☐	☐	☐	✓	☐
nurse	☐	☐	☐	✓	☐	☐	☐	☐
police officer	☐	☐	☐	☐	☐	✓	☐	☐
salesperson	☐	☐	☐	☐	✓	☐	☐	☐
security guard	☐	✓	☐	☐	☐	☐	☐	☐
singer	✓	☐	☐	☐	☐	☐	☐	☐

Source: Interviews with people between the ages of 17 and 55

Which opinions do you agree with? Which do you disagree with? Why?
Add your opinions to the chart. Check (✓) one adjective for each job.

7 CONVERSATION *That's exciting!*

▶ Listen and practice.

Richard: Hey, Stephanie. I hear you have a new job.
Stephanie: Yes. I'm teaching math at Lincoln High School.
Richard: How do you like it?
Stephanie: It's great. The students are terrific. How are things with you?
Richard: Not bad. I'm a firefighter now, you know.
Stephanie: That's exciting!
Richard: Yes, but it's a very stressful job. And sometimes it's dangerous.

8 LISTENING *It's pretty boring.*

▶ Listen. What do these women think of their jobs? Write the correct adjective.

1
.... *boring* ....

2
....

3
....

4
....

⑨ GRAMMAR FOCUS

Placement of adjectives ▶

be + adjective	**adjective + noun**
A firefighter's job **is dangerous**.	A firefighter has **a dangerous job**.
A doctor's job **is stressful**.	A doctor has **a stressful job**.

an athlete

A *Pair work* Say each sentence a different way.

1. A musician's job is interesting.
   "A musician has an interesting job."
2. An athlete's job is exciting.
3. A lawyer's job is stressful.
4. A security guard has a boring job.
5. A photographer has a difficult job.
6. A police officer has a dangerous job.

a photographer

B *Group work* Think of one job for each adjective. Do your classmates agree?

a police officer

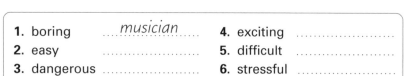

1. boring	*musician*	**4.** exciting	....
2. easy	....	**5.** difficult	....
3. dangerous	....	**6.** stressful	....

A: A musician has a boring job.
B: I don't really agree. A musician does *not* have a boring job.
C: You're right. A musician's job is very exciting.

⑩ INTERCHANGE 8 *The perfect job*

What do you want in a job? Go to Interchange 8.

⑪ WORKDAY ROUTINES

Group work Ask three classmates about their jobs (or their friends' or family members' jobs). Then tell the class.

Ask about a classmate
Do you have a job?
Where do you work?
What do you do, exactly?
Is your job interesting?
What time do you start work?
When do you finish work?
Do you like your job?
What do you do after work? . . .

Ask about a classmate's friend or family member
Tell me about your . . .
Where does he / she work?
What does he / she do, exactly?
Is his / her job difficult?
What time does he / she start work?
When does he / she finish work?
Does he / she like his job?
What does he / she do after work? . . .

Job Profiles

Look at the photos. Which job looks the best? Why?

actress

Lisa Parker has two jobs. She works as a waitress at night, but she's really an actress. During the day, she auditions for plays and television shows. Her schedule is difficult, and she's tired a lot. But she's following her dream.

video game tester

Lots of teenagers want **John Blue**'s job. He plays video games for eight hours a day. And he gets paid for it! John is a video game tester for a big video game company. Is it ever boring? Never. John almost always wins!

dog walker

Becky Peck walks in the park every day for many hours – rain or shine. Becky is a professional dog walker. She walks dogs for other people. Sometimes she takes 20 dogs to the park at one time!

teacher

Carlos Ruiz is a busy man. He plans lessons, grades homework, helps with after-school activities – and of course, he teaches! His salary isn't great, but that's OK. His students like his class, so he's happy.

A Read the article. Who says these things? Write your guesses.

1. "After I win, I take a break."   ....
2. "I don't usually work in the summer."   ....
3. "The restaurant closes late – around 2:00 A.M."   ....
4. "After work, my feet and arms are tired!"   ....

B Write a short description of a job, but don't write the name of the job. Then read it to the class. Your classmates guess the job.

Units 7-8 Progress check

SELF-ASSESSMENT

How well can you do these things? Check (✓) the boxes.

I can	Very well	OK	A little
Ask and answer simple present yes/no questions (Ex. 1)	☐	☐	☐
Talk about apartments and furniture using *there is/there are* (Ex. 1)	☐	☐	☐
Ask simple present Wh-questions about jobs (Ex. 2)	☐	☐	☐
Listen to and understand descriptions of jobs (Ex. 3)	☐	☐	☐
Give opinions about jobs using adjectives and nouns (Ex. 4)	☐	☐	☐

1 A NEW APARTMENT

A Imagine you are moving into this apartment. What things are in the rooms? Draw pictures. Use the furniture in the box and your own ideas.

bed	desk	lamp	sofa
chairs	dresser	mirror	table

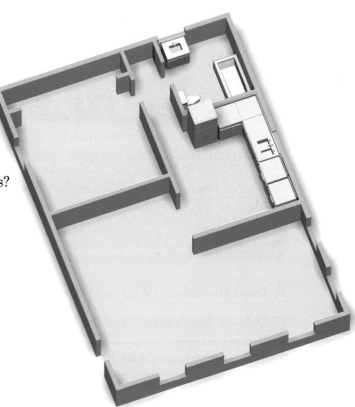

B *Pair work* Ask questions about your partner's apartment.

A: I'm moving into a new apartment!
B: That's great! Where is it?
A: . . .
B: What's it like? Does it have many rooms?
A: Well, it has . . . .
B: Does the . . . have . . . ?
A: . . .
B: Do you have a lot of furniture?
A: Well, there's . . . in the . . . .
   There are some . . . in the . . . .
B: Do you have everything you need for
   the apartment?
A: No, I don't. There's no . . . .
   There isn't any . . . .
   There aren't any . . . .
B: OK. Let's go shopping this weekend!

WHERE DOES HE WORK?

A Complete the conversations with Wh-questions.

1. A: *Where does your father work* ?
   B: My father? He works in a store.
   A: .... ?
   B: He's a salesperson.
   A: .... ?
   B: He likes his job a lot!

2. A: .... ?
   B: I'm an accountant.
   A: .... ?
   B: I work in an office.
   A: .... ?
   B: It's OK. I guess I like it.

B *Pair work* Your partner asks the questions in part A.
Answer with your own information.

 ## LISTENING *Where do they work?*

▶ Listen to Linda, Kyle, and Wendy talk about their jobs.
Check (✓) the correct answers.

	Where do they work?		What do they do?	
1. Linda	☐ office	☐ store	☐ receptionist	☐ doctor
2. Kyle	☐ school	☐ hospital	☐ nurse	☐ teacher
3. Wendy	☐ restaurant	☐ hospital	☐ manager	☐ cook

④ AN INTERESTING JOB

Group work What do you think of these jobs?
Give your opinions.

teacher

bus driver

farmer

hairstylist

A: I think a teacher has an interesting job.
B: I don't really agree. I think a teacher's job is boring.
C: Well, I think a teacher's job is stressful. . . .

WHAT'S NEXT?

Look at your Self-assessment again. Do you need to review anything?

9 Broccoli is good for you.

1 WORD POWER Foods

A ▶ Listen and practice.

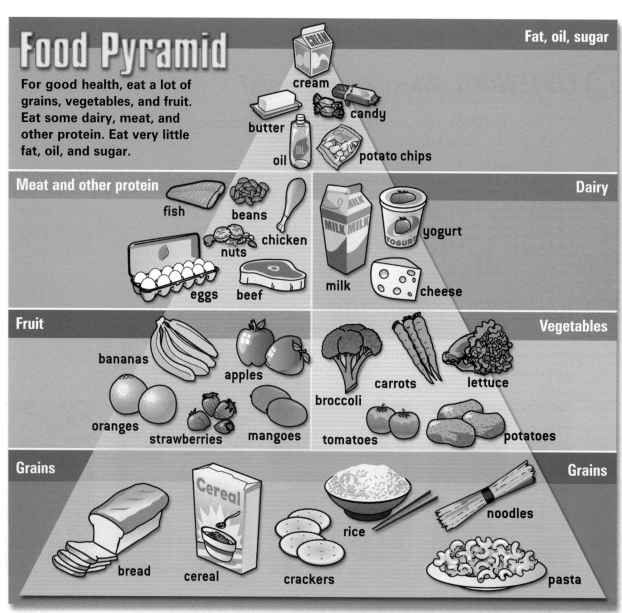

Food Pyramid

For good health, eat a lot of grains, vegetables, and fruit. Eat some dairy, meat, and other protein. Eat very little fat, oil, and sugar.

Fat, oil, sugar
- cream
- butter
- candy
- oil
- potato chips

Meat and other protein
- fish
- beans
- chicken
- nuts
- eggs
- beef

Dairy
- milk
- yogurt
- cheese

Fruit
- bananas
- apples
- oranges
- strawberries
- mangoes

Vegetables
- broccoli
- carrots
- lettuce
- tomatoes
- potatoes

Grains
- bread
- cereal
- crackers
- rice
- noodles
- pasta

Source: Adapted from the U.S. Department of Agriculture Food Guide Pyramid

B What foods do you like? What foods don't you like? Make a list. Then tell a partner.

A: I like rice, potato chips, and carrots.
I don't like fish, cheese, and bananas.
B: I like . . .

I like	I don't like
rice	fish
potato chips	cheese
carrots	bananas

58

② CONVERSATION *How about some sandwiches?*

A ▶ Listen and practice.

Adam: What do you want for the picnic?
Amanda: Hmm. How about some sandwiches?
Adam: OK. We have some chicken in the refrigerator, but we don't have any bread.
Amanda: And we don't have any cheese.
Adam: Do we have any drinks?
Amanda: No, we need some.
Adam: All right. Let's get some lemonade.
Amanda: And let's buy some potato salad.
Adam: Sure. Everyone likes potato salad.

B ▶ Listen to the rest of the conversation.
Check (✓) the desserts Adam and Amanda want.

☐ fruit salad   ☐ cake   ☐ pie   ☐ cookies   ☐ ice cream

③ GRAMMAR FOCUS

Some *and* any; *count and noncount nouns* ▶

Do we need **any** eggs?	*Count nouns*	*Specific*
Yes. Let's get **some** (eggs).	**an** egg → egg**s**	I'm eating **an egg.**
No. We don't need **any** (eggs).	**a** sandwich → sandwich**es**	Let's get **some bread.**
Do we need **any** bread?	*Noncount nouns*	*General*
Yes. Let's get **some** (bread).	bread	**Eggs are** good for you.
No, we do**n't** need **any** (bread).	lemonade	**Bread is** good for you.

A Complete the conversation with *some* or *any*.

Amanda: The store doesn't have ...*any*... potato salad.
Adam: Well, we have lots of potatoes. Let's make .... !
Amanda: OK. Do we have .... mayonnaise?
Adam: No, we need to buy ....
Amanda: We need .... onions, too.
Adam: Oh, I don't want .... onions. I hate onions!
Amanda: Then let's get .... celery.
Adam: No, I don't want .... celery in my potato salad. But let's put .... apples in it.
Amanda: Apples in potato salad? That sounds awful!

B Complete the chart with foods from Exercise 1 on page 58.

Count	Noncount
potatoes	*broccoli*

C *Group work* Look at your chart from part B. What foods are good for you? What foods are bad for you? Make general statements.

A: Broccoli is good for you, but potatoes are bad for you.
B: Are you sure? I think potatoes are good for you. . . .

 PRONUNCIATION *Sentence stress*

A ▶ Listen and practice. Notice the stressed words.

A: What do you need?

B: I need some bread and some fish.

A: Do you need any fruit?

B: Yes. I want some bananas.

B Make a list of foods you need. Then compare with a partner.

5 **SNAPSHOT**

▶ Listen and practice.

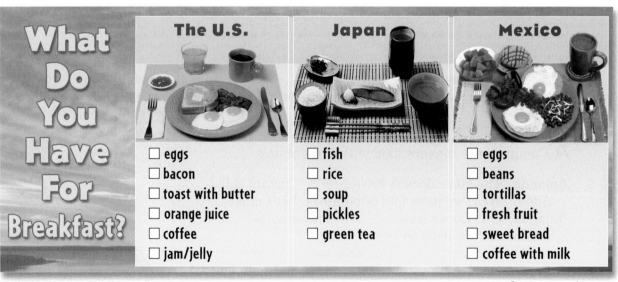

Source: *www.about.com*

What do you have for breakfast? Check (✓) the foods.
What else do you have for breakfast?

6 CONVERSATION *Fish for breakfast?*

 Listen and practice.

Sarah: Let's have breakfast together on Sunday.
Kumiko: OK. Come to my house. My family always
has a Japanese-style breakfast on Sundays.
Sarah: Really? What do you have?
Kumiko: We usually have fish, rice, and soup.
Sarah: Fish for breakfast? That's interesting.
Kumiko: Sometimes we have a salad, too.
And we always have green tea.
Sarah: Well, I never eat fish for breakfast,
but I like to try new things.

7 GRAMMAR FOCUS

Adverbs of frequency

always	
usually	
often	
I **sometimes** eat breakfast.	
hardly ever	
never	

Sometimes I eat breakfast.

Do you **ever** have fish for breakfast?
  Yes, I **always** do.
  Sometimes I do.
  No, I **never** do.

100%	always
	usually
	often
	sometimes
	hardly ever
0%	never

A Put the adverbs in the correct places. Then practice
with a partner.

usually
A: What do you ˄have for breakfast? (usually)
        ˄
B: Well, I have coffee, cereal, and juice. (often)
A: Do you eat breakfast at work? (ever)
B: I have breakfast at my desk. (sometimes)
A: Do you eat rice for breakfast? (usually)
B: No, I have rice. (hardly ever)

B Unscramble the sentences.

1. I have breakfast on never weekends
2. work I snacks eat at hardly ever
3. eat for pasta dinner sometimes I
4. have I dinner with often family my

I never have breakfast on weekends.
....
....
....

C Rewrite the sentences from part B with your own information.
Then compare with a partner.

A: I always have breakfast on weekends.
B: I hardly ever have breakfast on weekends. I usually get up late.

Broccoli is good for you. • 61

8 LISTENING *Really? Never?*

A  Paul and Megan are talking about food. How often does Megan eat these foods? Listen and check (✓) Often, Sometimes, or Never.

	Often	Sometimes	Never
pasta	✓	☐	☐
hamburgers	☐	☐	☐
fish	☐	☐	☐
eggs	☐	☐	☐
broccoli	☐	☐	☐

B *Group work* Do you ever eat the foods in part A? Tell your classmates.

A: I often eat pasta.
B: Really? I never eat pasta.
C: Well, I . . .

9 MEALTIME HABITS

A Add three questions about mealtime habits to the chart. Then ask a partner the questions and complete the chart.

Mealtime habits	Breakfast	Lunch	Dinner
1. Do you usually eat . . . ?	....	....	....
2. What time do you usually eat . . . ?	....	....	....
3. Do you ever eat meat for . . . ?	....	....	....
4. Do you ever go to a restaurant for . . . ?	....	....	....
5. What do you usually drink for . . . ?	....	....	....
6. What is something you never eat for . . . ?	....	....	....
7.	....	....	....
8.	....	....	....
9.	....	....	....

A: Kiyoshi, do you usually eat breakfast?
B: No, I hardly ever do.

B *Class activity* Tell your classmates about your partner's mealtime habits.

"Kiyoshi hardly ever eats breakfast. But he always eats lunch and dinner. . . ."

10 INTERCHANGE 9 *Food survey*

Complete a food survey. Go to Interchange 9 at the back of the book.

Eating for Good Luck

On special occasions, do you ever eat any of the foods in these pictures?

On New Year's Day, many people eat special foods for good luck in the new year.

Some Chinese people eat tangerines. Tangerines are round. Round foods end and begin again, like years.

It is a Jewish custom to eat apples with honey for a sweet new year.

Greeks eat *vasilopitta*, bread with a coin inside. Everyone tries to find the coin for luck and money in the new year.

In Spain and some Latin American countries, people eat 12 grapes at midnight on New Year's Eve – one grape for good luck in each month of the new year.

On New Year's Day in Japan, people eat *mochi* – rice cakes – for strength in the new year.

Some Americans from southern states eat black-eyed peas and rice with collard greens. The black-eyed peas are like coins, and the greens are like dollars.

A Read the article. Then correct these sentences.

1. Some Chinese people eat tangerines. Tangerines are ~~sweet~~ *round*, like years.
2. Some Jewish people eat apples with candy for a sweet new year.
3. Greeks eat *vasilopitta*, bread with beans inside.
4. In Europe, people eat 12 grapes for good luck in the new year.
5. The Japanese eat chocolate cake for strength in the new year.
6. Some Americans eat black-eyed peas. Black-eyed peas are like dollars.

B *Group work* Do you eat anything special on New Year's Day for good luck?
Do you do anything special? Tell your classmates.

10 I can't ice-skate very well.

1 SNAPSHOT

▶ Listen and practice.

Sports Seasons in the U.S. and Canada

In the spring, people . . . .
- ☐ play golf
- ☐ play soccer

In the summer, people . . . .
- ☐ play baseball
- ☐ play tennis
- ☐ play volleyball
- ☐ go swimming

In the fall, people . . . .
- ☐ play football
- ☐ go bike riding
- ☐ go hiking

In the winter, people . . . .
- ☐ play hockey
- ☐ play basketball
- ☐ go ice-skating
- ☐ go skiing

Sources: Adapted from *ESPN Information Please Sports Almanac*;
interviews with people between the ages of 18 and 50

What sports are popular in your country? Check (✓) the sports.
Do you like sports? What sports do you play or watch?

2 CONVERSATION *I love sports.*

A ▶ Listen and practice.

Lauren: So, Justin, what do you do in your free time?
Justin: Well, I love sports.
Lauren: Really? What sports do you like?
Justin: Hmm. Hockey, baseball, and soccer
are my favorites.
Lauren: Wow, you're a really good athlete!
When do you play all these sports?
Justin: Oh, I don't *play* these sports.
I just watch them on television!

B *Pair work* What do you do in your free time?
Tell your partner.

3 GRAMMAR FOCUS

What sports do you play?	I play **hockey** and **baseball**.
Who do you play baseball **with**?	I play with **some friends from work**. We have a team.
Where do you play?	We play **at Hunter Park**.
How often do you practice?	We practice **once or twice a week**.
When do you practice?	We practice **on Sundays**.
What time do you start?	We start **at ten o'clock in the morning**.

A Complete the conversations with the correct Wh-question words. Then practice with a partner.

1. A: I watch sports on television every weekend.
   B: Really? ...*What sports*... do you like to watch?
   A: Soccer. It's my favorite!
   B: .... do you usually watch soccer?
   A: On Sunday afternoons.
   B: And .... do you usually watch it? At home?
   A: No, at my friend's house. He has a really big television!

2. A: .... do you go bike riding?
   B: Oh, about once a month.
   A: I love to go bike riding. I go every Sunday.
   B: Really? .... do you go?
   A: Usually at about one o'clock.
   B: Oh, yeah? .... do you usually go with?
   A: My sister. Come with us next time!

B Complete the conversation with questions. Then compare with a partner.

A: *What sports do you like* .... ?
B: I like a lot of sports, but I really love volleyball!
A: .... ?
B: I usually play with my sister and some friends.
A: .... ?
B: We practice on Saturdays.
A: .... ?
B: We start at about noon.
A: .... ?
B: We usually play in our yard, but sometimes we play at the beach.

C *Pair work* Ask your partner five questions about sports. Then tell the class.

A: What sports do you like?
B: I like baseball and soccer.
A: When do you play baseball? . . .

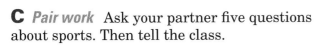

4 LISTENING What sports do you like?

 Listen to the conversations about sports. Complete the chart.

Favorite sport		Do they play or watch it?	
		Play	Watch
1. Lisa	*tennis*	✓	☐
2. John		☐	☐
3. Sue		☐	☐
4. Henry		☐	☐

5 CONVERSATION I can't sing.

 Listen and practice.

Kayla: Oh, look. There's a talent contest on Saturday. Let's enter.
Philip: I can't enter a talent contest. What can I do?
Kayla: You can sing really well.
Philip: Oh, thanks. . . . Well, you can, too.
Kayla: Oh, no. I can't sing at all – but I can play the piano.
Philip: So maybe we *can* enter the contest.
Kayla: Sure. Why not?
Philip: OK. Let's practice tomorrow!

6 PRONUNCIATION Can and can't

A Listen and practice. Notice the pronunciation of **can** and **can't**.

/kən/   /kænt/
I **can** act, but I **can't** sing very well.

B *Pair work* Your partner reads a sentence from the left or right column. Check (✓) the sentence you hear.

1. ☐ I can sing.   ☐ I can't sing.
2. ☐ I can act.   ☐ I can't act.
3. ☐ I can dance.   ☐ I can't dance.
4. ☐ I can swim.   ☐ I can't swim.

7 GRAMMAR FOCUS

Can *for ability* ▷

I			you			I		What **can** I do?
You			I			you		You **can** sing.
He	**can**	sing very well.	**Can**	he	sing?	Yes,	he	**can**.
She	**can't**	sing at all.		she		No,	she	**can't**.
We			we			we		Who **can** sing?
They			they			they		Philip **can**.

Additional header: "Yes," / "No," rows, and "Who **can** sing? Philip **can.**"

A Kayla is talking about things she can and can't do. Complete these sentences. Then compare with a partner.

1. I *can't* draw.

2. I .... act.

3. I .... sing.

4. I .... fix cars.

5. I .... play tennis.

6. I .... ice-skate very well.

7. I .... play the piano.

8. I .... cook at all.

B *Pair work* Ask and answer questions about the pictures in part A.

A: Can Kayla draw?
B: No, she can't.

C *Group work* Can your classmates do the things in part A? Ask and answer questions.

A: Can you draw, Pedro?
B: No, I can't. How about you, Sachiko?
C: I can't draw. But I can act!

I can't ice-skate very well. • **67**

8 LISTENING *I can do that!*

▶ Listen to three people talk about their abilities.
Check (✓) the things they can do well.

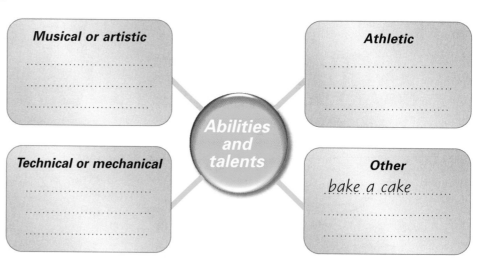

1. Peter	☐	☐	☐	☐	☐	☐	☐	☐
2. Liz	☐	☐	☐	☐	☐	☐	☐	☐
3. Scott	☐	☐	☐	☐	☐	☐	☐	☐

9 WORD POWER

A ▶ Complete the word map with abilities and talents from the list.
Then listen and check.

✓ bake a cake
design a Web page
do gymnastics
fix a car
fix a motorcycle
paint pictures
play chess
play the violin
ride a horse
sing English songs
surf
tell good jokes

Musical or artistic
....
....
....

Athletic
....
....
....

Abilities and talents

Technical or mechanical
....
....
....

Other
bake a cake ....
....
....

B *Group work* Who can do the things in part A?
Make a list of guesses about your classmates.

A: Who can bake a cake?
B: I bet Sophie can.
C: Who can design a Web page? . . .

bake a cake – Sophie
design a Web page –

C *Class activity* Go around the room and check your guesses.

A: Sophie, can you bake a cake?
B: Yes, I can.

10 INTERCHANGE 10 *Hidden talents*

Learn more about your classmates' hidden talents.
Go to Interchange 10 at the back of the book.

Race the U.S.!

How many different kinds of races can you think of?

Read about four unique American races.

Climb the stairs of New York City's Empire State Building in the **Empire State Building Run-Up!**

The climb is 1,050 feet (320 meters) – 86 floors, or 1,575 steps.

Winners can reach the top in just 10 to 11 minutes. Can you?

Take eight or ten days to **Race Across America** from Irvine, California, to Savannah, Georgia.

Cross the entire U.S. in this 2,900-mile (4,667 kilometer) bicycle race.

In this race, there are no "time-outs" for sleep. For eight to ten days, racers can sleep only about three hours each day!

Race on the exciting white waters of the Arkansas River in the **Downriver Race**.

Winners complete the 25.7 miles (41.5 kilometers) in just two hours!

This is the longest downriver race in the U.S. One person. One boat. Take the challenge!

Only possible in Alaska ... the **Iditarod Sled Dog Race**.

Race from downtown Anchorage to Nome – over 1,150 miles (1,850 kilometers) through cold, wind, and snow.

Winners usually finish the course in 9 to 12 days and receive cash prizes!

A Read the article. Then complete the chart.

	Places	Distances	Winning times
1. Empire State Building Run-Up			
2. Race Across America			
3. Downriver Race			
4. Iditarod Sled Dog Race			

B *Group work* Make up a race. What is it called? Where is it? What is the distance? What can you win?

Units 9-10 Progress check

SELF-ASSESSMENT

How well can you do these things? Check (✓) the boxes.

I can	Very well	OK	A little
Talk about foods using *some* and *any* (Ex. 1)	☐	☐	☐
Talk about eating habits using adverbs of frequency (Ex. 2)	☐	☐	☐
Listen to and understand questions about sports (Ex. 3)	☐	☐	☐
Ask and answer simple present Wh-questions (Ex. 4)	☐	☐	☐
Talk about job abilities using *can* (Ex. 5)	☐	☐	☐

1 CLASS PICNIC

Group work Plan a class picnic. Choose two main dishes, two salads, two drinks, and two desserts. Then tell the class.

Main dishes	
Salads	
Drinks	
Desserts	

useful expressions

Do we want any . . . ?
Let's get / make some . . .
I don't want / like . . .

2 SNACK SURVEY

Pair work Does your partner ever eat these snacks?
Ask questions and complete the survey.

	always	usually	sometimes	hardly ever	never
1. popcorn	☐	☐	☐	☐	☐
2. cookies	☐	☐	☐	☐	☐
3. chocolate	☐	☐	☐	☐	☐
4. bananas	☐	☐	☐	☐	☐
5. potato chips	☐	☐	☐	☐	☐
6. apples	☐	☐	☐	☐	☐

A: Do you ever have popcorn as a snack?
B: Yes, I aways have popcorn. OR No, I never have popcorn.

3 *LISTENING* *What do you play?*

 Listen to Jenny ask Ben about sports. Check (✓) Ben's answers.

1. ☐ I play baseball.　　　3. ☐ At 6:30 P.M.　　　5. ☐ On the weekends.
　 ☐ I play basketball.　　　　 ☐ At 6:30 A.M.　　　　 ☐ In the afternoons.

2. ☐ Some friends from school.　4. ☐ Every day.　　　6. ☐ At the park.
　 ☐ Some friends from work.　　　 ☐ Every week.　　　　 ☐ In the yard.

4 *WHAT DO YOU LIKE?*

A Complete the chart with things you love, like, and don't like.

	I love . . .	I like . . .	I don't like . . .
Sports	....	....	....
Foods	....	....	....
Clothes	....	....	....

B *Pair work* Find out what your partner loves, likes, and doesn't like. Then ask more questions with *who*, *where*, *how often*, or *when*.

A: What sports do you love?
B: I love ice-skating.
A: Who do you usually go ice-skating with? . . .

5 *JOB ABILITIES*

Group work What can these people do well? Make a list.
Use the abilities in the box and your own ideas. Then tell the class.

chef

mechanic

artist

musician

bake
cook
draw
fix a car
fix a motorcycle
paint
play the piano
read music

A: A chef can cook very well.
B: A chef can also bake things, like cakes.
C: Also, a chef can . . .

WHAT'S NEXT?

Look at your Self-assessment again. Do you need to review anything?

11 What are you going to do?

1 MONTHS AND DATES

A Listen. Practice the months and the dates.

Months	Dates		
January	1st first	11th eleventh	21st twenty-first
February	2nd second	12th twelfth	22nd twenty-second
March	3rd third	13th thirteenth	23rd twenty-third
April	4th fourth	14th fourteenth	24th twenty-fourth
May	5th fifth	15th fifteenth	25th twenty-fifth
June	6th sixth	16th sixteenth	26th twenty-sixth
July	7th seventh	17th seventeenth	27th twenty-seventh
August	8th eighth	18th eighteenth	28th twenty-eighth
September	9th ninth	19th nineteenth	29th twenty-ninth
October	10th tenth	20th twentieth	30th thirtieth
November			31st thirty-first
December			

B *Class activity* Go around the room.
Make a list of your classmates' birthdays.

A: Anna, when's your birthday?
B: July 21st. When's *your* birthday?

My classmates' birthdays
Anna – July 21st

2 CONVERSATION *Happy birthday!*

 Listen and practice.

Angie: Are you going to do anything exciting
this weekend?
Philip: Well, I'm going to celebrate my birthday.
Angie: Fabulous! When is your birthday, exactly?
Philip: It's August ninth – Sunday.
Angie: So what are your plans?
Philip: Well, my friend Kayla is going to
take me out for dinner.
Angie: Nice! Is she going to order a cake?
Philip: Yeah, and the waiters are probably
going to sing "Happy Birthday"
to me. It's so embarrassing.

The future with be going to ▶

Are you **going to do** anything this weekend?	Yes, I am. I**'m going to celebrate** my birthday.
	No, I'm not. I**'m going to stay home**.
Is Kayla **going to have** a party for you?	Yes, she is. She**'s going to invite** all my friends.
	No, she isn't. She**'s going to take** me **out** for dinner.
Are the waiters **going to sing** to you?	Yes, they are. They**'re going to sing** "Happy Birthday."
	No, they aren't. But they**'re going to give** me a cake.

A What are these people going to do this weekend?
Write sentences. Then compare with a partner.

1. *They're going to go dancing.*
2. *She's going to read.*

B *Pair work* Is your partner going to do the things in part A
this weekend? Ask and answer questions.

A: Are you going to go dancing this weekend?
B: Yes, I am. I'm going to go to a new dance club downtown.
A: Are you going to go with a friend? . . .

INTERCHANGE 11 Guessing game

Make guesses about your classmates' plans. Go to Interchange 11.

5 PRONUNCIATION *Reduction of going to*

A Listen and practice. Notice the reduction of **going to** to /gənə/.

A: Are you **going to** have a party?　　A: Are you **going to** go to a restaurant?
B: No, I'm **going to** go out with a friend.　B: Yes. We're **going to** go to Nick's Café.

B *Pair work* Ask your partner about his or her weekend plans. Try to reduce **going to**.

6 LISTENING *Evening plans*

A It's 5:30 P.M. What are these people's evening plans? Write your guesses in the chart.

B Listen to the interviewer ask these people about their plans. What are they really going to do? Complete the chart.

Michelle　Kevin　Robert　Jane

Your guess	What they're really going to do
Michelle *is going to go to the gym* .	**Michelle** ....
Kevin	**Kevin** ....
Robert	**Robert** ....
Jane	**Jane** ....

7 SNAPSHOT

Listen and practice.

Source: *The Concise Columbia Encyclopedia*

Do you celebrate any of these holidays? How do you celebrate them?
What are some holidays in your country? What's your favorite holiday?

8 CONVERSATION *Have a good Valentine's Day.*

Listen and practice.

Mona: So, Tyler, are you going to do anything special for Valentine's Day?

Tyler: Yeah, I'm going to take my girlfriend out for dinner.

Mona: Oh, really? Where are you going to go?

Tyler: Laguna's. It's her favorite restaurant.

Mona: Oh, she's going to like that!

Tyler: How about you? What are you going to do?

Mona: Well, I'm not going to go to a restaurant, but I am going to go to a dance.

Tyler: Sounds like fun. Well, have a good Valentine's Day.

Mona: Thanks. You, too.

9 GRAMMAR FOCUS

Wh-questions with be going to

What are you going to do for Valentine's Day?
  I'm going to go to a dance.
  I'm not going to go to a restaurant.
Where are you going to go?
  We**'re going to go** to Laguna's.
  We**'re not going to stay** home.

How are you going to get there?
  We**'re going to drive.**
  We**'re not going to take** a bus.
Who's going to be there?
  My friends **are going to be** there.
  My sister **isn't going to be** there.

A Complete this conversation with the correct form of *be going to.*
Then practice with a partner.

A: What ..*are*.. you ...*going to do*...... (do) for Halloween?
B: I don't know. I .... (not do) anything special.
A: Well, Pat and I .... (have) a party. Can you come?
B: Sure! Where .... you .... (have) the party?
A: It .... (be) at Pat's house.
B: What time .... the party .... (start)?
A: At 6:00. And it .... (end) around midnight.
B: Who .... you .... (invite)?
A: We .... (ask) all our good friends.

B *Group work* Ask your classmates about their plans.
Use the time expressions in the box.

A: What are you going to do tonight?
B: I'm going to go to a party.
C: Oh, really? Who's going to be there?
B: Well, Lara and Rosa are going to come.
   But Jeff isn't going to be there. . . .

time expressions	
tonight	next week
tomorrow	next month
tomorrow night	next summer

A ▶ Listen and practice. Then check (✓) the things you do for each special occasion.

	Mother's Day	Father's Day	Graduation	Wedding	Anniversary
send cards	☐	☐	☐	☐	☐
give presents	☐	☐	☐	☐	☐
take pictures	☐	☐	☐	☐	☐
sing songs	☐	☐	☐	☐	☐
dance	☐	☐	☐	☐	☐
eat cake	☐	☐	☐	☐	☐
have a party	☐	☐	☐	☐	☐
have a picnic	☐	☐	☐	☐	☐
eat special food	☐	☐	☐	☐	☐
wear special clothes	☐	☐	☐	☐	☐

B *Group work* What special occasions are you going to celebrate this year? When are they? How are you going to celebrate them? Ask your classmates.

A: What special occasions are you going to celebrate this year?
B: I'm going to go to my sister's wedding.
C: Really? When is she going to get married?

HOLIDAYS AND FESTIVALS

A *Pair work* Choose any holiday or festival you like. Then ask and answer these questions.

What is the holiday or festival?
When is it?
What are you going to do?
Where are you going to go?
Who's going to be there?
When are you going to go?
How are you going to get there?

A: What is the holiday or festival?
B: It's Cinco de Mayo.
A: When is it?
B: It's on May fifth.
A: What are you going to do?
B: I'm going to go to a parade. . . .

B *Class activity* Tell the class about your partner's plans.

Cinco de Mayo in Mexico

Setsubun in Japan

Eid in Pakistan

What are you going to do on your birthday?

Elena Buenaventura
Madrid
"My twenty-first birthday is on Saturday, and I'm going to go out with some friends. To wish me a happy birthday, they're going to pull on my ear 21 times – once for each year. It's an old custom. Some people pull on the ear just once, but my friends are very traditional!"

Yan-ching Shi
Taipei
"Tomorrow is my sixteenth birthday. It's a special birthday, so we're going to have a family ceremony. I'm probably going to get some money in 'lucky' envelopes from my relatives. My mother is going to cook noodles – noodles are for a long life."

Mr. and Mrs. Aoki
Kyoto
"My husband is going to be 60 tomorrow. In Japan, the sixtieth birthday is called *kanreki* – it's the beginning of a new life. The color red represents a new life, so children often give something red as a present. What are our children going to give him? A red hat and vest!"

Philippe Joly
Paris
"I'm going to be 30 next week, so I'm going to invite three very good friends out to dinner. In France, when you have a birthday, you often invite people out. In some countries, I know it's the opposite – people take you out."

A Read the article. Then correct these sentences.

1. To celebrate her birthday, Elena is going to pull on her friends' ears.
2. Yan-Ching is going to cook some noodles on her birthday.
3. On his birthday, Mr. Aoki is going to buy something red.
4. Philippe's friends are going to take him out to dinner on his birthday.

B *Group work* How do people usually celebrate birthdays in your country? Do you have plans for your next birthday? How about the birthday of a friend or family member? What are you going to do? Tell your classmates.

12 What's the matter?

1 WORD POWER Parts of the body

A ▶ Listen and practice.

head
eye
ear
nose

mouth
tooth/teeth
chin

back
shoulder
chest
stomach

wrist
arm
elbow

throat
neck

thumb
hand
finger(s)

leg
knee
ankle

foot/feet
toe(s)

B *Pair work* Close your books. Tell your partner to point to the parts of the body.

A: Point to your neck.
B: This is my neck.
    Point to your feet.
A: These are my feet.

② CONVERSATION *I feel homesick.*

▶ Listen and practice.

Brian: Hey, Kenichi. How are you?
Kenichi: Oh, I'm not so good, actually.
Brian: Why? What's the matter?
Kenichi: Well, I have a headache. And a backache.
Brian: Maybe you have the flu.
Kenichi: No, I think I just feel a little homesick for Japan.
Brian: That's too bad. . . . But maybe I can help. Let's have lunch at that new Japanese restaurant.
Kenichi: That's a great idea. Thanks, Brian. I feel better already!

③ GRAMMAR FOCUS

Have + *noun;* feel + *adjective* ▶

What's the matter? What's wrong? **I have a headache.** **I have a backache.** **I have the flu.**	How are you? How do you feel? **I feel homesick.** **I feel better.** **I don't feel well.**	Negative adjectives sick awful terrible miserable	Positive adjectives fine great terrific fantastic

A ▶ Listen and practice. *"He has a backache."*

a backache   an earache   a headache   a stomachache   a toothache

a cold   a cough   a fever   the flu   sore eyes   a sore throat

B *Pair work* Act out a health problem. Your partner guesses the problem.

A: What's wrong? Do you have a headache?
B: No, I don't.
A: Do you have an earache?
B: Yes, that's right!

What's the matter? • 79

C *Class activity* Go around the class. Find out how your classmates feel today. Respond with an expression from the box.

A: How do you feel today, Jun?
B: I feel fine, thanks. What about you, Leo?
A: I feel terrible. I have a stomachache.
B: I'm sorry to hear that.

4 LISTENING *I have a headache.*

A ▶ Listen to the conversations. Where do these people hurt? Write down the parts of the body.

1. Ben
   head, throat ....
2. Alison ....
3. Jeffrey ....
4. Marta ....

B *Pair work* Ask and answer questions about the people in part A.

A: What's the matter with Ben?
B: He has a headache and a sore throat.

5 SNAPSHOT

▶ Listen and practice.

Sources: Based on information from *Almanac of the American People* and interviews with people between the ages of 25 and 50

What medications do you have at home?
What are these medications for?

6 CONVERSATION Don't work too hard.

Listen and practice.

Dr. Young: Hello, Ms. West. How are you today?
Ms. West: Not so good.
Dr. Young: So, what's wrong, exactly?
Ms. West: I'm exhausted!
Dr. Young: Hmm. Why are you so tired?
Ms. West: I don't know. I just can't sleep at night.
Dr. Young: OK. Let's take a look at you.

A few minutes later

Dr. Young: I'm going to give you some pills.
Take one pill every night after dinner.
Ms. West: OK.
Dr. Young: And don't drink coffee, tea, or soda.
Ms. West: Anything else?
Dr. Young: Yes. Don't work too hard.
Ms. West: All right. Thanks,
Dr. Young.

7 LISTENING Let's take a look.

Listen to Dr. Young talk to four other patients. What does she give them? Check (✓) the correct medications.

	Antacid	Aspirin	Cold pills	Eye drops	Muscle cream
1. Ben	☐	☐	☐	☐	☐
2. Alison	☐	☐	☐	☐	☐
3. Jeffrey	☐	☐	☐	☐	☐
4. Marta	☐	☐	☐	☐	☐

8 PRONUNCIATION Sentence intonation

A Listen and practice. Notice the intonation in these sentences.

Take some aspirin.   Don't drink coffee.

Go to bed.   Don't work too hard.

Use some muscle cream.   Don't exercise this week.

B *Pair work* Practice the conversation in Exercise 6 again.
Pay attention to the sentence intonation.

What's the matter? • **81**

9 GRAMMAR FOCUS

Imperatives

Take a pill every four hours.   **Don't work** too hard.
Rest in bed.   **Don't stay up** late.
Drink lots of juice.   **Don't drink** soda.

A Complete these sentences. Use the correct forms of the words in the box.

✓ call	see	not go	not drink
listen	take	✓ not worry	not eat

1. .....*Call*..... a dentist.   5. .... to relaxing music.
2. ...*Don't worry*... too much.   6. .... a doctor.
3. .... two aspirin.   7. .... coffee.
4. .... to school.   8. .... any candy.

B Write two pieces of advice for each problem. Use the sentences from part A or your own ideas.

 (I have a toothache.)

 (I have a headache.)

 (I have the flu.)

(I can't sleep at night.)

1. *Call a dentist.* 2. .... 3. .... 4. ....
....

C *Pair work* Act out the problems from part B. Your partner gives advice.

A: I feel miserable!
B: What's the matter?
A: I have a terrible toothache!
B: I have an idea. Call a dentist. . . .

10 INTERCHANGE 12 Helpful advice

Give advice for some common problems. Go to Interchange 12.

10 Simple Ways to Improve Your Health

Can you think of some ways to improve your health? Don't look at the article.

Believe it or not, you can greatly improve your health in ten simple ways.

1 Eat breakfast. Breakfast gives you energy for the morning.

2 Go for a walk. Walking is good exercise, and exercise is necessary for good health.

3 Floss your teeth. Don't just brush them. Flossing keeps your gums healthy.

4 Drink eight cups of water every day. Water helps your body in many ways.

5 Stretch for five minutes. Stretching is important for your muscles.

6 Wear a seat belt. Every year, seat belts save thousands of lives.

7 Do something to challenge your brain. For example, do a crossword puzzle or read a new book.

8 Protect your skin. Use lots of moisturizer and sunscreen.

9 Get enough calcium. Your bones need it. Dairy foods, like yogurt, milk, and cheese, have calcium.

10 Take a "time-out" – a break of about 20 minutes. Do something different. For example, get up and walk. Or sit down and listen to music.

Source: *Cooking Light* ® Magazine

A Read the article. Then complete the sentences.

1. To get exercise, *go for a walk* .
2. To help your bones, .
3. To help your muscles, .
4. To keep your gums healthy, .
5. To have energy for the morning, .
6. To challenge your brain, .

B *Group work* What things in the article do you do regularly?
What else do you do for your health? Tell your classmates.

Units 11–12 Progress check

SELF-ASSESSMENT

How well can you do these things? Check (✓) the boxes.

I can	Very well	OK	A little
Ask and answer yes/no questions about holidays with *be going to* (Ex. 1)	☐	☐	☐
Ask and answer Wh-questions about future plans with *be going to* (Ex. 2)	☐	☐	☐
Use future time expressions (Ex. 2)	☐	☐	☐
Listen to and understand conversations about problems (Ex. 3)	☐	☐	☐
Talk about problems using *have* + noun and *feel* + adjective (Ex. 4)	☐	☐	☐
Give advice using imperatives (Ex. 4)	☐	☐	☐

1 HOLIDAY SURVEY

A Complete the questions with names of different holidays.

Are you going to . . . ?	Name
dance on	....
give presents on	....
have a party on	....
send cards on	....
take photos on	....

B *Class activity* Are your classmates going to do the things in part A? Go around the class and find this information. Try to write a different name on each line.

2 PLANS, PLANS, PLANS

Complete these questions with different time expressions.
Then ask a partner the questions.

1. How are you going to get home *tonight* .... ?
2. What time are you going to go to bed .... ?
3. Who's going to be here .... ?
4. Where are you going to go .... ?
5. What are you going to do .... ?
6. Who are you going to eat dinner with .... ?

LISTENING What's the matter?

Listen to six conversations. Number the pictures from 1 to 6.

.... This person needs some ketchup.

.... This person has a backache.

.... This person can't dance very well.

...1... This person feels sad.

.... This person is going to take a test tomorrow.

.... This person has the flu.

④
THAT'S GREAT ADVICE!

A Write a problem on a piece of paper. Then write advice for the problem on a different piece of paper.

| I'm homesick. | | Call your family. |

B *Class activity* Put the papers with problems and the papers with advice in two different boxes. Then take a new paper from each box. Go around the class and find the right advice for your problem.

A: I feel terrible.
B: What's the matter?
A: I'm homesick.
B: Maybe I can help. See a dentist.
A: That's terrible advice!

A: I feel awful.
C: Why? What's wrong?
A: I'm homesick.
C: I know! Call your family.
A: That's great advice. Thanks!

WHAT'S NEXT?

Look at your Self-assessment again. Do you need to review anything?

13 You can't miss it.

WORD POWER Places and things

A ▶ Where can you get these things? Match the things with the places. Then listen and practice. *"You can buy aspirin at a drugstore."*

1. aspirin ...*b*...
2. bread ....
3. a dictionary ....
4. gasoline ....
5. a sandwich ....
6. stamps ....
7. a sweatshirt ....
8. traveler's checks ....

a. a bank

b. a drugstore

c. a post office

d. a gas station

e. a restaurant

f. a bookstore

g. a department store

h. a supermarket

B *Pair work* What else can you get or do in the places in part A? Make a list.

A: You can get money at a bank.
B: You can also . . .

2 **LISTENING** *I need a new swimsuit.*

A Listen to the Anderson family's conversations. What do they need? Where are they going to buy them? Complete the chart.

	What	Where
1. Jean	*a swimsuit*	....
2. Mom	....	*the supermarket*
3. Dad	....	....
4. Mike	....	....

B *Pair work* What do you need? Where are you going to buy it? Tell your partner.

"I need a dictionary, so I'm going to go to a bookstore. . . ."

3 **CONVERSATION** *It's across from the park.*

 Listen and practice.

Man: Excuse me. Can you help me? Is there a public rest room around here?

Woman: A public rest room? Hmm. I'm sorry. I don't think so.

Man: Oh, no. My son needs a rest room.

Woman: Well, there's a rest room in the department store on Main Street.

Man: Where on Main Street?

Woman: It's on the corner of Main and First Avenue.

Man: On the corner of Main and First?

Woman: Yes, it's across from the park. You can't miss it.

Man: Thanks a lot.

4 **PRONUNCIATION** *Compound nouns*

Listen and practice. Notice the stress in these compound nouns.

post office   gas station   rest room   coffee shop

drugstore   supermarket   bookstore   department store

You can't miss it. • **87**

Prepositions of place ▶

| on | on the corner of | across from | next to | between |

The department store is **on** Main Street.
It's **on the corner of** Main and First.
It's **across from** the park.

It's **next to** the bank.
The bank is **between** the department store **and** the restaurant.

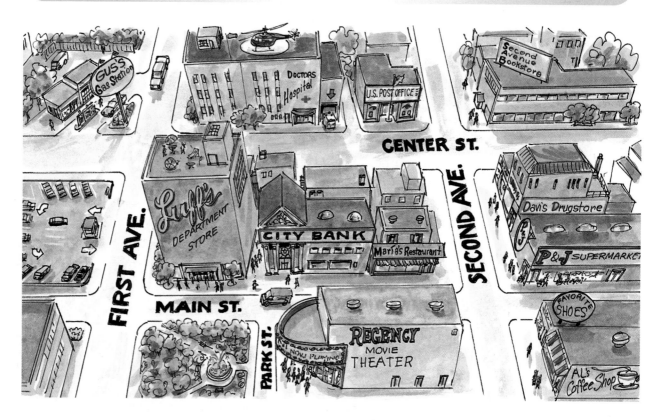

A Look at the map and complete the sentences. Then compare with a partner.

1. The coffee shop is ......*on*....... Second Avenue. It's .... the shoe store.
2. The movie theater is .... Park and Main. It's .... the park.
3. The gas station is .... the parking lot. It's .... First and Center.
4. The drugstore is .... Center and Second. It's .... the supermarket.
5. The bank is .... the restaurant and the department store.
   It's .... Main Street.

B *Pair work* Where are these places on the map? Ask and answer questions.

the park   the post office   the bookstore   the hospital   the shoe store

A: Where is the park?
B: It's between Park and First, across from the department store.

6 LISTENING *Where is it?*

▶ Look at the map in Exercise 5. Listen to four conversations.
Where are the people going?

1. *the bank*   2. ....   3. ....   4. ....

7 SNAPSHOT

▶ Listen and practice.

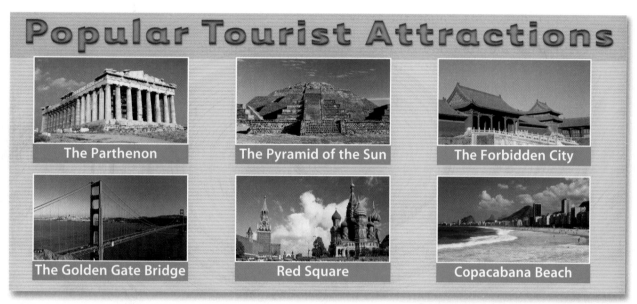

Popular Tourist Attractions

The Parthenon

The Pyramid of the Sun

The Forbidden City

The Golden Gate Bridge

Red Square

Copacabana Beach

Sources: *www.infoplease.com; www.fodors.com*

Where are these places? What do you know about them?
What tourist attractions in your country are popular? Why?

8 CONVERSATION *Is it far from here?*

▶ Listen and practice.

Tourist: Excuse me, ma'am. Can you help me?
How do I get to St. Patrick's Cathedral?
Woman: Just walk up Fifth Avenue to 50th Street.
St. Patrick's is on the right.
Tourist: Is it near Rockefeller Center?
Woman: Yes, it's right across from
Rockefeller Center.
Tourist: Thank you. And where is the
Empire State Building?
Is it far from here?
Woman: It's right behind you.
Just turn around and look up!

⑨ GRAMMAR FOCUS

Directions ▶

How do I get to Rockefeller Center?	How can I get to Bryant Park?
Walk up/Go up Fifth Avenue.	**Walk down/Go down** Fifth Avenue.
Turn left on 49th Street.	**Turn right on** 42nd Street.
It's **on the right**.	It's **on the left**.

Pair work Imagine you are tourists at Grand Central Terminal.
Ask for directions. Follow the arrows.

A: Excuse me. How do I get to the Empire State Building?
B: Walk up 42nd Street. Turn . . .

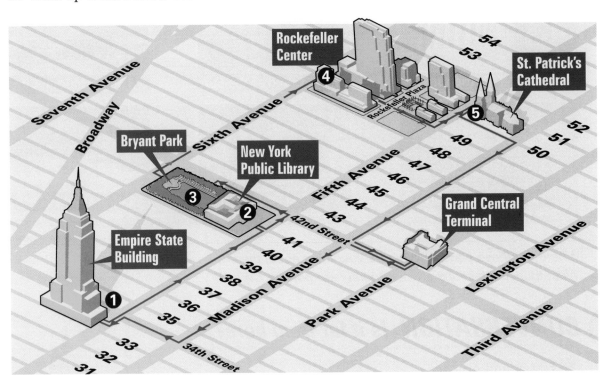

⑩ YOUR NEIGHBORHOOD

A Draw a map of your neighborhood.

B *Pair work* Look at your partner's map. Ask for directions
to places in your partner's neighborhood.

A: How do I get to the bookstore?
B: Walk . . .

⑪ INTERCHANGE 13 *Giving directions*

Give directions. Student A find Interchange 13A; Student B find Interchange 13B.

A Walk Up Fifth Avenue

As you read, look at the map in Exercise 9.

1 Start your tour at the **Empire State Building** on Fifth Avenue between 33rd and 34th Streets. This building has 102 floors. Take the elevator to the 102nd floor for a great view of New York City.

2 Now walk up Fifth Avenue seven blocks to the **New York Public Library**. The entrance is between 40th and 42nd Streets. This library holds over 10 million books. Behind the library is **Bryant Park**. In the summer, there's an outdoor café, and at lunch hour, there are free music concerts.

3 Walk up Sixth Avenue to 49th Street. You're standing in the middle of the 19 buildings of **Rockefeller Center**. Turn right on 49th Street, walk another block, and turn left. You're in **Rockefeller Plaza**. In the winter, you can ice-skate in the rink there.

4 Right across from Rockefeller Center on Fifth Avenue is **St. Patrick's Cathedral**. It's modeled after the cathedral in Cologne, Germany. Go inside St. Patrick's and leave the noisy city behind. Look at the beautiful blue windows. Many of these windows come from France.

A Read the tourist information. Where can you . . . ?

1. listen to music outdoors   ....
2. go ice-skating in the winter   ....
3. sit quietly indoors   ....
4. get a view of the city   ....

B *Group work* Ask the questions in part A.
Answer with information about your city or town.

A: Where can you listen to music outdoors?
B: You can listen to music in the park next to the river.
C: Or you can . . .

14 Did you have fun?

SNAPSHOT

▶ Listen and practice.

Top Eight Things People Hate to Do

1. stand in line
2. do laundry
3. travel to work
4. go to meetings
5. exercise
6. work in the yard
7. clean the house
8. open the mail

Source: Based on information from *The Book of Lists*

Do you hate to do these things?
What other things do you hate to do? Why?

CONVERSATION *I didn't study!*

▶ Listen and practice.

Michael: Hi, Jennifer. Did you have a good weekend?
Jennifer: Well, I had a busy weekend, and I feel a little tired today.
Michael: Really? Why?
Jennifer: Well, on Saturday, I exercised in the morning. Then my roommate and I cleaned, did laundry, and shopped. And then I visited my parents.
Michael: So what did you do on Sunday?
Jennifer: I studied for the test all day.
Michael: Oh, no! Do we have a test today? I didn't study! I just watched television all weekend!

3 GRAMMAR FOCUS

Simple past statements: regular verbs ▶

I	**studied**	on Sunday.		I	**didn't study**	on Saturday.
You	**watched**	television.		You	**didn't watch**	a movie.
She	**stayed**	home.		She	**didn't stay**	out.
We	**shopped**	for groceries.		We	**didn't shop**	for clothes.
They	**exercised**	on Saturday.		They	**didn't exercise**	on Sunday.

did**n't** = did not

Spelling

watch → watch**ed**
exercise → exercis**ed**
study → stud**ied**
stay → stay**ed**
shop → shop**ped**

A Tim is talking about his weekend. Complete the sentences. Then compare with a partner.

On Friday night, I ....*waited*.... (wait) for a phone call, but my girlfriend ..*didn't call*.. (not call). I just .... (stay) home and .... (watch) television. On Saturday, I .... (visit) my friend Frank. We .... (talk) and .... (listen) to music. In the evening, he .... (invite) some friends over, and we .... (cook) a great meal. I .... (not work) very hard on Sunday. I .... (not study) at all. I just .... (walk) to the mall and .... (shop).

B Complete the sentences. Use your own information. Then compare with a partner.

1. Yesterday, I *watched / didn't watch* (watch) television.
2. Last night, I .... (stay) home.
3. Last week, I .... (exercise) every day.
4. Last month, I .... (shop) for clothes.
5. Last year, I .... (visit) a different country.

4 PRONUNCIATION Simple past -ed endings

A ▶ Listen and practice. Notice the pronunciation of **-ed**.

/t/	/d/	/ɪd/
work**ed**	clean**ed**	invit**ed**
watch**ed**	stay**ed**	visit**ed**
....	....	....
....	....	....

B ▶ Listen and write these verbs under the correct sounds.

cooked   exercised   listened   needed   shopped   waited

Did you have fun? • 93

5 GRAMMAR FOCUS

Simple past statements: irregular verbs ▶

I **did** my homework.
I **didn't do** laundry.

You **got up** at noon.
You **didn't get up** at 10:00.

He **went** to the museum.
He **didn't go** to the library.

We **met** our classmates.
We **didn't meet** our teacher.

You **came** home late.
You **didn't come** home early.

They **had** a picnic.
They **didn't have** a party.

A ▶ Complete the chart. Then listen and check.

Present	Past	Present	Past	Present	Past
buy	bought	....	read /rɛd/	....	sat
....	ate	....	rode	....	took
....	felt	....	saw	....	wore

For a list of more irregular verbs, see the appendix at the back of the book.

B *Pair work* Did you do the things in the pictures yesterday? Tell your partner.

"Yesterday, I did my homework. I also did laundry. . . ."

6 LAST WEEKEND

A Write five things you *did* and five things you *didn't do* last weekend.

B *Group work* Tell your classmates about your weekend.

A: I saw a movie last weekend.
B: I didn't see a movie. But I watched television.
C: I watched television, too! I saw . . .

Things I did	Things I didn't do
I saw a movie.	I didn't exercise.
I studied.	I didn't buy clothes.

7 CONVERSATION Did you like it?

▶ Listen and practice.

Laura: So, did you go anywhere last summer?
Erica: Yes, I did. My sister and I went to Arizona.
We saw the Grand Canyon.
Laura: Really? Did you like it?
Erica: Oh, yes. We loved it!
Laura: Did you go hiking there?
Erica: No, we didn't. Actually, we rode horses.
And we also went white-water rafting on
the Colorado River!
Laura: Wow! Did you have fun?
Erica: Yes, we did. We had a great time!

8 GRAMMAR FOCUS

Simple past yes/no questions ▶

Did you **have** a good summer?
    Yes, I **did**. I **had** a great summer.
Did you **play** volleyball?
    No, I **didn't**. I **played** tennis.

Did Erica **like** her vacation?
    Yes, she **did**. She **liked** it a lot.
Did Erica and her sister **go** to Colorado?
    No, they **didn't**. They **went** to Arizona.

A Complete the conversations. Then practice with a partner.

1. A: ...*Did*... you ..*have*.. (have) a good summer?
   B: Yes, I .... I .... (have) a great
      summer. I just .... (relax).

2. A: .... you .... (go) anywhere last summer?
   B: No, I .... I .... (stay) here. But my
      friends .... (visit) me, and on the weekends
      we .... (go out) a lot.

3. A: .... you .... (take) any classes last summer?
   B: Yes, I .... I .... (take) tennis lessons,
      and I .... (play) tennis every day!

4. A: .... you .... (speak) English last summer?
   B: No, I .... But I .... (read) English
      books and I .... (watch) English movies.

B *Pair work* Ask the questions from part A.
Answer with your own information.

A: Did you have a good summer?
B: No, I didn't. I just stayed home. . . .

9 LISTENING I didn't go anywhere.

▶ Listen to Andy, Gail, Patrick, and Fran. What did they do last summer? Check (✓) the correct answers.

1. Andy	☐ stayed home	✓ visited his brother	☐ went to the beach
2. Gail	☐ saw movies	☐ read books	☐ watched television
3. Patrick	☐ went bike riding	☐ went jogging	☐ played tennis
4. Fran	☐ studied	☐ had a job	☐ painted the house

10 WORD POWER Summer activities

A ▶ Find two words from the list that go with each verb in the chart. Then listen and check.

a class   a picnic
fun   pictures
✓ hiking   a play
a movie   ✓ swimming
new people   tennis
old friends   volleyball

go	*hiking*	*swimming*
have	....	....
meet	....	....
play	....	....
see	....	....
take	....	....

B *Pair work* Check (✓) six things to ask your partner. Then ask and answer questions.

Did you . . . last summer?

☐ go anywhere interesting	☐ play any games
☐ buy anything interesting	☐ read any books
☐ eat any new foods	☐ see any movies
☐ meet any interesting people	☐ take any pictures
☐ exercise or play any sports	☐ wear different clothes
☐ work	☐ have fun

A: Did you go anywhere interesting last summer?
B: Yes, I did. I went to the beach almost every day, and . . .

C *Class activity* Tell the class about your partner's summer.

"Last summer, Maria went to the beach almost every day. She . . ."

11 INTERCHANGE 14 Past and present

Are you different now from when you were a child? Go to Interchange 14.

WEEKEND STORIES

Scan the article. Who had a terrible weekend? Who enjoyed the weekend? Who learned a lot over the weekend?

Kelly

"I had a great weekend. I went to my best friend Helen's wedding. She got married at home. All her friends and family went. She looked fantastic! She wore a beautiful dress. After the ceremony, her parents served a wonderful meal. I'm really happy for her. And I really like her husband!"

Robert

"I had an awful weekend. My friends and I went to a rock concert. I had a terrible time! It took three hours to drive there. I didn't like the music at all! And after the concert ended, our car broke down! I called my parents, and they came and got us. We finally got home at ten this morning. I am so tired!"

Erin

"I had an interesting weekend. I went camping for the first time. My friends took me. We left on Saturday and drove to the campsite. First, we put up the tent. Then we built a fire, cooked dinner, and told stories. We got up early on Sunday and went fishing. I caught a fish! I didn't really like camping, but I learned a lot."

A Read the article. Then correct these sentences.

1. Kelly got married. *Kelly's best friend got married* .
2. Helen got married in a church. .
3. After the wedding, everyone went out to eat. .
4. Robert went to a rock concert with his parents. .
5. It took three hours to get home after the concert. .
6. Robert got home at ten o'clock last night. .
7. Erin goes camping every weekend. .
8. Erin and her friends went fishing on Saturday. .
9. Erin liked camping a lot. .

B *Group work* Do you have a story about a wedding, rock concert, or camping trip? Write four sentences about it. Then tell your classmates.

Units 13-14 Progress check

SELF-ASSESSMENT

How well can you do these things? Check (✓) the boxes.

I can	Very well	OK	A little
Listen to and understand conversations about places and things (Ex. 1)	☐	☐	☐
Ask and answer questions about places using prepositions of place (Ex. 2)	☐	☐	☐
Ask for and give directions (Ex. 2)	☐	☐	☐
Talk about your last vacation using simple past (Ex. 3)	☐	☐	☐
Ask and answer simple past yes/no questions about last weekend (Ex. 4)	☐	☐	☐

1 LISTENING *What are you looking for?*

▶ Listen to the conversations. What do the people need?
Where can they get or find it? Complete the chart.

What	Where
1.	....
2.	....
3.	....
4.	....

2 WHERE IS THE . . . ?

A *Pair work* Are these places near your school? Where are they?
Ask and answer questions.

bank	coffee shop	hospital	post office
bookstore	department store	park	supermarket

A: Where is the bank?
B: It's on Second Avenue. It's across from the Korean restaurant.

B *Pair work* Give directions from your school to the places in part A.
Your partner guesses the place.

A: Walk up First Avenue and turn left. It's on the right, on the corner
of First and Lincoln.
B: It's the coffee shop.
A: That's right!

3 MY LAST VACATION

A Write four statements about your last vacation.
Two are true and two are false.

	I went to London.
	I saw a play.
	I didn't take any pictures.
	I didn't go to a museum.

B *Pair work* Read your statements. Your partner says
"True" or "False." Who has more correct guesses?

A: On my last vacation, I went to London.
B: False.
A: That's right. It's false. OR Sorry. It's true.

4 LAST WEEKEND

A Check (✓) the things you did last weekend.
Then add two more things you did.

☐ saw a movie	☐ had dinner at a restaurant
☐ worked in the yard	☐ read a book
☐ cleaned the house	☐ went dancing
☐ exercised or played sports	☐ met some interesting people
☐ went shopping	☐ talked on the phone
☐ bought some clothes	☐ got up late
☐ saw friends	☐ ....
☐ studied	☐ ....

B *Pair work* Ask your partner about his or her weekend.

A: Did you see a movie last weekend, Keiko?
B: Yes, I did. I saw the new Tom Cruise movie.
   I loved it. Did you see a movie?
A: No, I didn't. . . .

C *Group work* Join another pair. Tell them about
your partner's weekend.

"Keiko saw the new Tom Cruise movie. She loved it. . . ."

WHAT'S NEXT?

Look at your Self-assessment again. Do you need to review anything?

15 Where were you born?

1 SNAPSHOT

▶ Listen and practice.

WHERE WERE THESE PEOPLE BORN?

1. ____ Issey Miyake, designer

2. ____ Shakira, singer

3. ____ Chow Yun Fat, actor

4. ____ Salma Hayek, actress

5. ____ Ronaldo, athlete

a. Brazil
b. China
c. Colombia
d. Japan
e. Mexico

Answers: 1. d   2. c   3. b   4. e   5. a

Sources: *www.biography.com; www.celebrities.net.cn; www.salma.com*

Match the people with the countries. Then check your answers at the bottom of the Snapshot. What famous people were born in your country? What do they do?

2 CONVERSATION *I was born in Korea.*

▶ Listen and practice.

Chuck: Where were you born, Melissa?
Melissa: I was born in Korea.
Chuck: Oh! So you weren't born in the U.S.
Melissa: No, I came here in 1999.
Chuck: Hmm. You were pretty young.
Melissa: Yes, I was only seventeen.
Chuck: Did you go to college right away?
Melissa: No, my English wasn't very good, so I took English classes for two years first.
Chuck: Well, your English is really good now.
Melissa: Thanks. Your English is pretty good, too.
Chuck: Yeah, but I was born here.

GRAMMAR FOCUS

Statements with the past of be

I **was** born in Korea.	I **wasn't** born in the U.S.	**Contractions**
You **were** pretty young.	You **weren't** very old.	wasn't = was not
She **was** seventeen.	She **wasn't** in college.	weren't = were not
We **were** born in the same year.	We **weren't** born in the same country.	
They **were** in Korea in 1998.	They **weren't** in the U.S. in 1998.	

A Melissa is talking about her family. Choose the correct verb forms. Then compare with a partner.

My family and I ..*were*.. (was / were) all born in Korea – we .... (wasn't / weren't) born in the U.S. I .... (was / were) born in the city of Inchon, and my brother .... (was / were) born there, too. My parents .... (wasn't / weren't) born in Inchon. They .... (was / were) born in the capital, Seoul.

Seoul

Questions with the past of be

Were you born in the U.S.?	**Where were** you born?
Yes, I **was**.	I **was** born in Korea.
No, I **wasn't**.	
Was your brother born in 1984?	**When was** he born?
Yes, he **was**.	He **was** born in 1985.
No, he **wasn't**.	
Were your parents born in Inchon?	**What city were** they born **in**?
Yes, they **were**.	They **were** born in Seoul.
No, they **weren't**.	

B Complete these questions with *was* or *were*.

1. ..*Were*.. you born in this city?
2. When .... you born?
3. Where .... your parents born?
4. When .... your mother born?
5. When .... your father born?
6. .... you and your family in this city last year?
7. .... you at this school last year?
8. Who .... your first English teacher?
9. What nationality .... your first English teacher?
10. What .... he or she like?

years
1906 (nineteen oh six)
1917 (nineteen seventeen)
1999 (nineteen ninety-nine)
2001 (two thousand and one)

C *Pair work* Ask and answer the questions from part B. Use your own information.

A: Were you born in this city?
B: No, I wasn't. I was born in Tokyo.

4 LISTENING *Where was she born?*

▶ Where were these people born? When were they born?
Listen and complete the chart.

Michelle Yeoh

Apolo Ohno

Gisele Bündchen

Gael García Bernal

	Place of birth	Year of birth
1. Michelle Yeoh	*Malaysia*	....
2. Apolo Ohno	....	....
3. Gisele Bündchen	....	....
4. Gael García Bernal	....	....

5 PRONUNCIATION *Negative contractions*

A ▶ Listen and practice.

one syllable		two syllables	
aren't	don't	isn't	doesn't
weren't	can't	wasn't	didn't

B ▶ Listen and practice.

They **didn't** eat dinner because they **weren't** hungry.
I **don't** like coffee, and she **doesn't** like tea.
These **aren't** their swimsuits. They **can't** swim.
He **wasn't** here yesterday, and he **isn't** here today.

C Write four sentences with negative contractions.
Then read them to a partner.

> *I didn't go because my friends weren't there.*

6 CONVERSATION *Where did you grow up?*

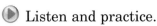 Listen and practice.

Melissa: So, Chuck, where did you grow up?
  Chuck: I grew up in Texas. I was born there, too.
Melissa: And when did you come to Los Angeles?
  Chuck: In 1990. I went to college here.
Melissa: Oh. What was your major?
  Chuck: Drama. I was an actor for
         five years after college.
Melissa: That's interesting.
         So why did you become
         a hairstylist?
  Chuck: Because I needed
         the money. And
         I love it. Look.
         What do you think?
Melissa: Well, uh . . .

7 GRAMMAR FOCUS

Wh-questions with *did, was, and* were

Where did you grow up?	I **grew up** in Texas.
When did you come to Los Angeles?	I **came** to Los Angeles in 1990.
Why did you become a hairstylist?	Because I **needed** the money.
How old were you in 1990?	I **was** eighteen.
What was your major in college?	It **was** drama.
How was college?	It **was** great.

A Match the questions with the answers. Then compare with a partner.

1. When and where were you born? ...c...
2. Where did you grow up? ....
3. When did you start school? ....
4. How old were you then? ....
5. How was your first day of school? ....
6. Who was your first friend in school? ....
7. What was he/she like? ....
8. Why did you take this class? ....

a. I was six.
b. She was really shy.
c. I was born in 1983 in Hiroshima, Japan.
d. Her name was Yumiko.
e. My English wasn't very good.
f. I grew up in Tokyo.
g. I entered first grade in 1989.
h. It was a little scary.

B *Pair work* Ask and answer the questions in part A.
Use your own information.

8 WORD POWER

A ▶ Complete the word map with words from the list. Then listen and check.

✓classroom
college
elementary
gym
high
history
junior high
lunchroom
math
physical education
playground
science

School days

Classes
....
....
....
....

Schools
....
....
....
....

Places
classroom
....
....
....

B *Pair work* Find out about your partner's elementary, junior high, or high school days. Ask these questions. Then tell the class.

What classes did you take?	Who was your favorite teacher? Why?
What was your favorite class? Why?	Who was your least favorite teacher? Why?
What was your least favorite class? Why?	Where did you spend your free time? Why?
Who was your best friend?	What did you like best?

"In elementary school, Dan spent his free time in the gym because he played a lot of sports. . . ."

9 FIRST DAY OF CLASS

A *Group work* Do you remember the first day of this class? Ask and answer these questions.

1. What did you wear?
2. Were you early, late, or on time?
3. Where did you sit?
4. How did you feel?
5. Who was the first person you met?
6. What did the teacher talk about?
7. Who talked the most? the least?
8. How was your English then? How is it now?

B *Class activity* What does your group remember? Tell the class.

10 INTERCHANGE 15 *Time line*

Make a time line of your life. Go to Interchange 15.

RICKY MARTIN

> Scan the article. What three cities did Ricky Martin live in?

Ricky Martin was born in San Juan, Puerto Rico, on December 24, 1971. He was always a performer. As a child, he appeared in television commercials and studied singing.

At the age of 12, he joined the Latin boy band, Menudo. He worked hard with them, and he became very well known. But he left the group after five years.

Martin moved to New York City, but he didn't work for a year. He was very frustrated, so he moved to Mexico City and got a part on a Mexican soap opera. Soon afterward, he recorded two Spanish-language albums. After this success, he moved back to the U.S.

Back in the U.S., he appeared on an American soap opera and in the Broadway show, *Les Miserables*. Then he made his first English-language album.

That album was called *Ricky Martin*. His biggest hit, "Livin' La Vida Loca," was on that album.

Now he's famous around the world. But he still works hard, and he still loves singing. As he said to a reporter for the newspaper *USA Today*: "I want to do this forever."

A Read the article. Then write a question for each answer.

1. .... ? In Puerto Rico.
2. .... ? At the age of 12.
3. .... ? After five years.
4. .... ? Because he was frustrated.
5. .... ? *Les Miserables*.
6. .... ? "Livin' La Vida Loca."

B Number these events in Ricky Martin's life from 1 (first event) to 10 (last event).

.... a. He joined a boy band.
.... b. He moved to New York City.
.... c. He made an English-language album.
.... d. He appeared in a Broadway musical.
.... e. He recorded albums in Spanish.

.... f. He returned to the U.S.
..1.. g. He was born.
.... h. He left Menudo.
.... i. He studied singing.
.... j. He moved to Mexico.

C *Group work* Who is your favorite singer? What do you know about his or her life? Tell your classmates.

16 Can she call you later?

1 CONVERSATION *I was in the shower.*

 Listen and practice.

Answering
machine: Hi. This is Jennifer, and this is Nicole.
We can't come to the phone right now.
Please leave us a message after the tone.
Michael: Hi. This is Michael. . . .
Nicole: Oh, hi, Michael. It's Nicole. Sorry I didn't
answer the phone right away. I was in
the shower.
Michael: That's OK. Is Jennifer there?
Nicole: No, she's at the mall. Can she call you later?
Michael: Yeah, thanks. Please ask her to call me
at home.
Nicole: Sure.
Michael: Thanks a lot, Nicole.

2 WORD POWER *Prepositional phrases*

A Listen and practice.

at home	**at the** mall	**in** bed	**in the** shower	**on** vacation
at work	**at the** library	**in** class	**in the** hospital	**on** a trip
at school	**at the** beach	**in** Mexico	**in the** yard	**on** his/her break

at the mall

in class

on vacation

B *Pair work* Make a list of five friends and family members.
Give it to your partner. Where are these people right now?
Ask and answer questions.

A: Where's your brother right now?
B: He's on vacation. He's in Thailand.

3 LISTENING *She's in the yard.*

A  Listen to people call Lisa, Jeff, Brenda, and Eric. Where are they? Complete the sentences.

1. Lisa is *in the yard* .   3. Brenda is ....
2. Jeff is ....   4. Eric is ....

B *Pair work* Call the people in part A.

A: Hello. Is Lisa there, please?
B: Yes, but she's in the yard.

4 GRAMMAR FOCUS

Subject and object pronouns ▷

Subjects		**Objects**
I		me
You		you
He		him
She got Michael's message.	Michael left	**her** a message.
We		us
They		them

A Complete the phone conversations with the correct pronouns. Then practice with a partner.

1. A: Can ...*I*... speak with Ms. Fee, please?
   B: .... 's not here. But maybe .... can help you.
   A: Please give .... my new phone number. It's 555-2981.

2. A: Hi, this is David. Is Mr. Roberts there?
   B: .... 'm sorry, but .... 's not here right now.
      Do you want to leave .... a message?
   A: Yes. Please tell .... to call me at work.

3. A: Hello, this is Carol's Café. Are Kate and Joe in?
   B: No, ... 're not. Can .... help you?
   A: .... found Kate and Joe's keys. .... left .... on the table.
   B: Just bring .... the keys. I can give .... to Kate and Joe.
   A: I'm sorry, but .... can't. Can Kate and Joe call .... ?
   B: OK.

B Write messages for three classmates. Then call a partner and leave each classmate a message.

A: Hello. Is Yuko in?
B: I'm sorry. She's at the library. Can I take a message?
A: Yes. Please tell her to meet me after class.

> *Yuko — Meet me*
> *after class.*

Can she call you later? • 107

⑤ SNAPSHOT

▶ Listen and practice.

Popular Activities in the U.S.

☐ go to the movies

☐ go to a concert

☐ visit an amusement park

☐ see a sports event

☐ go to an art festival

Sources: *The Encyclopedia Britannica*; The National Endowment for the Arts

Check (✓) the activities that are popular in your country.
What other activities are popular in your country?
What are your favorite activities? Why?

⑥ CONVERSATION *I'd love to!*

▶ Listen and practice.

Michael: Hello?
Jennifer: Hi, Michael. It's Jennifer. I got your message.
Michael: Hi. Thanks for calling me back.
Jennifer: So, what's up?
Michael: Uh, well, do you want to see a movie with me tomorrow night?
Jennifer: Tomorrow night? I'm sorry, but I can't. I have to study for a test.
Michael: Oh, that's too bad. How about Friday night?
Jennifer: Uh, . . . sure. I'd love to. What time do you want to meet?
Michael: How about around seven o'clock?
Jennifer: Terrific!

7 PRONUNCIATION Want to *and* have to

A ▶ Listen and practice. Notice the reduction of **want to** and **have to**.

/wanə/
A: Do you **want to** go to a party with me tonight?

/hæftə/
B: I'm sorry, I can't. I **have to** work late.

B *Pair work* Practice the conversation in Exercise 6 again. Try to reduce **want to** and **have to**.

go to a party

8 GRAMMAR FOCUS

> **Invitations; verb + to** ▶
>
> **Do you want to see** a movie with me tonight?
> Sure. I'**d** really **like to** see a good comedy.
> I'**d like** to (see a movie), but I **have to** study.
> I'**d** = I would
>
> **Would you like to go** to a soccer game?
> Yes, I'**d love to** (go to a soccer game)!
> I **want to** (go), but I **need to** work.

A Complete the invitations. Then match them with the responses.

Invitations

1. Would you ...*like to*... visit an amusement park this weekend? ...*d*...

2. Do you .... go to a basketball game tomorrow night? ....

3. Would you .... see a movie tonight? ....

4. Do you .... go swimming on Saturday? ....

5. Do you .... play soccer after school today? ....

6. Would you .... go to an art festival on Sunday afternoon? ....

Responses

a. I'd like to, but I don't have a swimsuit!

b. I'm sorry, but I have to talk to the teacher after school.

c. I don't really like basketball. Do you want to do something else?

d. I'd like to, but I can't. I'm going to go on a trip this weekend.

e. Yes, I'd love to. I love art festivals!

f. Tonight? I can't. I need to help my parents.

B *Pair work* Practice the invitations from part A. Respond with your own information.

A: Do you want to go to a basketball game tomorrow night?
B: I'd like to, but I can't. I have to work. . . .

9 EXCUSES, EXCUSES!

A Do you ever use these excuses? Check (✓) Often, Sometimes,
or Never. What are your three favorite excuses? Compare with a partner.

	Often	Sometimes	Never
I have to babysit.	☐	☐	☐
I need to study for a test.	☐	☐	☐
I have to work late.	☐	☐	☐
I need to go to bed early.	☐	☐	☐
I want to visit my family.	☐	☐	☐
I have a class.	☐	☐	☐
I have a headache.	☐	☐	☐
I'm not feeling well.	☐	☐	☐
I need to do laundry.	☐	☐	☐
I already have plans.	☐	☐	☐

B Write down three things you want to do this weekend.

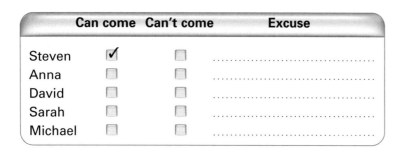

I want to go to the baseball game on Saturday.

I have to babysit.

C *Class activity* Go around the class and invite your classmates to
do the things from part B. Your classmates respond with excuses.

A: Would you like to go to the baseball game on Saturday?
B: I'm sorry, but I can't. I have to . . .

10 LISTENING I'd love to, but . . .

A ▶ Jennifer and Nicole invited some people to a party.
Listen to their answering machine messages. Who can come?
Who can't come? Check (✓) the correct answers.

	Can come	Can't come	Excuse
Steven	✓	☐	....
Anna	☐	☐	....
David	☐	☐	....
Sarah	☐	☐	....
Michael	☐	☐	....

B ▶ Listen again. Why can't some people come? Write their excuses.

11 INTERCHANGE 16 Let's make a date!

Make a date with your classmates. Go to Interchange 16.

MIAMI Florida

What's on This Saturday?

Look at the shows and events. Which do you want to go to? Number the pictures from 1 (most interesting) to 5 (least interesting).

IMAX Movie at the Museum of Discovery and Science

Shows at 4, 6, 8, and 10 P.M.

Do you want to travel, but don't have the money? Experience the world through the IMAX movie *The Greatest Places*. Seats in the theater sell out fast, so come early!

Animal Shows at Parrot Jungle Island

Open 10:00 A.M. to 6:00 P.M.

There are over 3,000 exotic animals and 100 plants at this beautiful nature park. Amazing animal tricks and outdoor animal shows, too.

Rock Concert on South Beach

7:00 P.M. to midnight

Come hear some great music under the stars! Five terrific bands are going to play. Sandwiches and soda sold.

Summer Fashion Show at Dolphin Mall

Starts at 3:00 P.M.

Men's and women's summer clothes. Seating is still available to see the latest fashions. All clothing is on sale after the show for under $100.

Art Festival at Broward Community College

9:00 A.M. to 5:00 P.M.

Need to buy a present? Check out this multicultural event. Find jewelry, paintings, clothing, and more! Food from around the world, too.

 Home

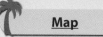 **Map**

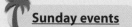 **Sunday events**

Contact us

A Read the Web page. Where can you do these things? Write two places.

1. buy clothes or jewelry ....
2. buy food ....
3. sit indoors ....
4. be outdoors ....
5. see a live performance ....

B *Group work* Where do you like to go in your city or town? What shows or events do you like? Tell your classmates.

Units 15-16 Progress check

SELF-ASSESSMENT

How well can you do these things? Check (✓) the boxes.

I can	Very well	OK	A little
Talk about your past using the past of *be* (Ex. 1)	☐	☐	☐
Ask about famous people using simple past yes/no questions (Ex. 2)	☐	☐	☐
Listen to and understand phone calls with subject and object pronouns (Ex. 3)	☐	☐	☐
Ask yes/no questions using verb + *to* (Ex. 4, 5)	☐	☐	☐
Make, accept, and refuse invitations (Ex. 5)	☐	☐	☐
Give excuses (Ex. 5)	☐	☐	☐

1 WHERE WERE YOU IN . . . ?

A *Pair work* Choose three years in your partner's life. Then ask your partner the questions and complete the chart.

	199___	199___	200___
How old were you in . . . ?	....	....	....
Where were you in . . . ?	....	....	....
What were you like in . . . ?	....	....	....

B *Class activity* Tell the class about your partner's life.

"In 1990, Raul was four. He . . ."

2 WHO WAS HE?

Group work Think of a famous person from the past. Your classmates ask yes/no questions to guess the person.

Was he/she born in . . . ?
Was he/she a singer? an actor?
Was he/she tall? heavy? good-looking?

A: I'm thinking of a famous man from the past.
B: Was he born in the U.S.?
A: No, he wasn't.
C: Was he . . . ?

Listen and check (✓) the best response.

1. ☐ Yes. Please tell her to call me.
   ☐ Yes. Please tell him to call me.

2. ☐ Yes. Does he have your number?
   ☐ No. He isn't here right now.

3. ☐ Yes, you do.
   ☐ No, I don't.

4. ☐ I'm going to visit my parents.
   ☐ I had a terrible headache.

5. ☐ I'm sorry, but I can't go.
   ☐ No, I didn't go. I was at work.

6. ☐ I'm sorry, he's not here right now.
   ☐ No, Sandra is at work right now.

4 **FIND SOMEONE WHO . . .**

A *Class activity* Go around the class. Ask questions to complete the chart. Try to write a different name on each line.

Find someone who . . .	Name
needs to do laundry this weekend	....
doesn't want to do homework tonight	....
has to babysit this week	....
would like to go shopping this weekend	....
wants to see a movie tonight	....
has to go to the doctor this week	....
needs to work this weekend	....
would like to go home early	....

A: Megumi, do you need to do laundry this weekend?
B: Yes, I do.

B *Pair work* Compare your answers with a partner.

5 **INVITATIONS**

A Make a list of five things you want to do this summer.

B *Class activity* Go around the class. Invite your classmates to do the things from part A. Your classmates accept or refuse the invitations.

A: Would you like to play tennis this summer?
B: I'm sorry, I can't. I have to . . . .

C: Do you want to go to an art festival this summer?
D: Sure, I'd love to! When would you like to . . . ?

WHAT'S NEXT?

Look at your Self-assessment again. Do you need to review anything?

Interchange activities

FAMOUS CLASSMATES

A Imagine you are a famous person. Write your name, phone number, and e-mail address on the card.

Name: *Ben Affleck*
Phone: *(646) 555-0831*
E-mail: *benaffleck@cup.org*

at   dot

Name: ....
Phone: ....
E-mail: ....

B *Class activity* Go around the class. Introduce yourself to three "famous people." Ask and answer questions to complete the cards.

A: Hi, my name is Drew Barrymore.
B: I'm Ben Affleck. Nice to meet you, Drew.
A: Ben, what's your e-mail address?
B: It's B-E-N-A-F-F-L-E-C-K at C-U-P dot O-R-G.
A: I'm sorry. Can you repeat that?

useful expressions
I'm sorry.
Can you repeat that?
How do you spell that?

Name: ....
Phone: ....
E-mail: ....

Name: ....
Phone: ....
E-mail: ....

Name: ....
Phone: ....
E-mail: ....

Interchange 1

FIND THE DIFFERENCES.

A *Pair work* How are the two pictures different? Ask questions to find the differences.

A: Where are the sunglasses?
B: In picture 1, they're on the television.
A: In picture 2, they're behind the television.

Picture 1

Picture 2

B *Class activity* Talk about the differences with your classmates.

"In picture 1, the sunglasses are on the television. In picture 2, they're . . ."

CELEBRITY FASHIONS

Group work Take turns. Describe the people at the party.
Don't say the person's name. Your classmates guess the person.

A: He's wearing blue jeans, a yellow shirt,
and a black jacket. Who is it?
B: Is it Marc Anthony?
A: No, it isn't.
C: Is it Will Smith?
A: That's right.

B: They're wearing dresses. Who are they?
C: Are they Reese Witherspoon and Nicole Kidman?
B: That's right.

Will Smith

Halle Berry

Penelope Cruz

Björk

Adam Sandler

Reese Witherspoon

Renée Zellweger

Interchange 4

Jennifer Lopez

Denzel Washington

Antonio Banderas

Keanu Reeves

Cameron Diaz

Nicole Kidman

Marc Anthony

Jackie Chan

Tom Cruise

BOARD GAME

A *Pair work* Play the board game. Follow these instructions.

1. Choose a marker. Place it on **Start**.
2. Student A tosses a coin and moves one or two spaces.

   "Heads" means move two spaces.
   "Tails" means move one space.

heads   tails

3. Student A makes a question with the words in the space.
   Student A asks Student B, and Student B answers.
4. The game continues. Student B tosses a coin and moves
   one or two spaces.
5. Continue until both markers are on **Finish**.

A: It's "heads." I move two spaces. What's your last name?
B: It's Lee. Now it's my turn!

useful expressions
It's your turn.
It's my turn.
I don't know.

B *Class activity* Tell the class two things about your partner.

"Mario's from Rome. Rome is very exciting and crowded."

WHAT'S WRONG WITH THIS PICTURE?

Group work What's wrong with this picture? Tell your classmates.

"Ellen is swimming, but she's wearing high heels and a hat!"

A *Class activity* Go around the class and find this information.
Try to write a different name on each line.

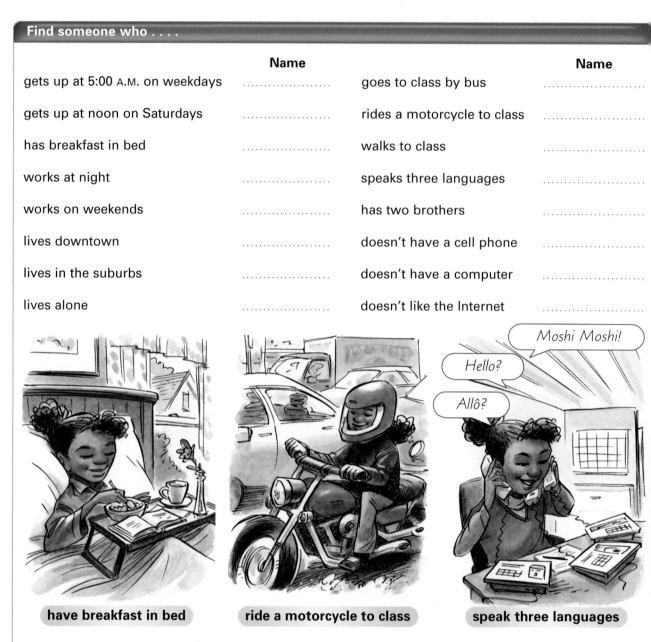

Find someone who . . . .

	Name		Name
gets up at 5:00 A.M. on weekdays	....	goes to class by bus	....
gets up at noon on Saturdays	....	rides a motorcycle to class	....
has breakfast in bed	....	walks to class	....
works at night	....	speaks three languages	....
works on weekends	....	has two brothers	....
lives downtown	....	doesn't have a cell phone	....
lives in the suburbs	....	doesn't have a computer	....
lives alone	....	doesn't like the Internet	....

Moshi Moshi!

Hello?

Allô?

have breakfast in bed   **ride a motorcycle to class**   **speak three languages**

A: Do you get up at 5:00 A.M. on weekends, Jung Ho?
B: No, I get up at 7:00 A.M.

A: Do you get up at 5:00 A.M. on weekdays, Keiko?
C: Yes, I get up at 5:00 A.M. every day.

B *Group work* Compare your answers.

A: Keiko gets up at 5:00 A.M.
B: Maria gets up at 5:00 A.M., too.
C: Jung Ho gets up at . . .

Interchange 6

FIND THE DIFFERENCES.

A *Pair work* Find the differences between Bill's apartment and Rachel's apartment.

Bill's apartment

Rachel's apartment

A: There are four chairs in Bill's kitchen, but there are three chairs in Rachel's kitchen.

B: There's a sofa in Bill's living room, but there's no sofa in Rachel's living room.

B *Group work* Compare your answers.

THE PERFECT JOB

A *Pair work* Imagine you're looking for a job. What do you want to do? First, check (✓) your answers to the questions. Then ask your partner the same questions.

Job survey	Me		My partner	
Do you want to . . . ?	**Yes**	**No**	**Yes**	**No**
talk to people	☐	☐	☐	☐
help people	☐	☐	☐	☐
perform in front of people	☐	☐	☐	☐
work from 9 to 5	☐	☐	☐	☐
use a computer	☐	☐	☐	☐
use the telephone	☐	☐	☐	☐
work at home	☐	☐	☐	☐
work outdoors	☐	☐	☐	☐
work in an office	☐	☐	☐	☐
have your own office	☐	☐	☐	☐
travel	☐	☐	☐	☐
wear a uniform	☐	☐	☐	☐
wear a suit	☐	☐	☐	☐
wear blue jeans	☐	☐	☐	☐
have an exciting job	☐	☐	☐	☐
have a relaxing job	☐	☐	☐	☐

work from 9 to 5

work outdoors

work at home

perform in front of people

travel

B *Pair work* Think of a good job for your partner.

A: You want to perform in front of people, travel, and wear blue jeans. Do you want to be a pop singer?
B: No, a pop singer's job is very stressful.
A: Well, do you want to be . . .

FOOD SURVEY

A Complete the food survey. Use these foods and other foods you know.

Things I	eat every day	eat twice a week	eat once a week	never eat
meat/fish				
dairy				
fruits				
vegetables				
snacks				

B *Pair work* Compare your information.

A: I eat onions every day.
B: I never eat onions, but I eat chocolates every day.

A *Class activity* Go around the class. Find someone who *can* and someone who *can't* do each thing. Try to write a different name on each line.

Names		
Can you . . . ?	**Can**	**Can't**
play three musical instruments	....	....
dance the tango	....	....
say "Hello" in five languages	....	....
swim underwater	....	....
write with both hands	....	....
do a handstand	....	....
fix a computer	....	....
juggle	....	....
sew your own clothes	....	....
do magic tricks	....	....

dance the tango   write with both hands   do a handstand

juggle   sew your own clothes   do magic tricks

A: Can you play three musical instruments?
B: Yes, I can. OR No, I can't.

B *Class activity* Share your answers with the class.

"Mei-Li can't play three musical instruments, but Claudia can.
She can play the guitar, violin, and piano."

Interchange 10

A *Pair work* Is your partner going to do any of these things? Check (✓) your guesses.

Is your partner going to . . . ?	My guesses		My partner's answers	
	Yes	No	Yes	No
1. watch television tonight	☐	☐	☐	☐
2. study English this evening	☐	☐	☐	☐
3. use a computer tomorrow	☐	☐	☐	☐
4. cook dinner tomorrow night	☐	☐	☐	☐
5. go out with friends this weekend	☐	☐	☐	☐
6. eat at a restaurant this weekend	☐	☐	☐	☐
7. go to the gym next week	☐	☐	☐	☐
8. buy something expensive this month	☐	☐	☐	☐
9. go on a trip next month	☐	☐	☐	☐
10. visit family next summer	☐	☐	☐	☐

B *Pair work* Ask and answer questions to check your guesses.

A: Are you going to watch television tonight?
B: Yes, I am. I'm going to watch a movie.

C *Class activity* How many of your guesses are correct?
Who has the most correct guesses?

A *Pair work* Imagine you have these problems. Your partner gives advice.

I can't lose weight. I really like dessert. Cake is my favorite food!

1

My job is very stressful. I usually work 10 hours a day and on weekends.

2

I can never get up on time in the morning. I'm always late for school.

3

I'm new in town, and I don't know any people here. How can I make some friends?

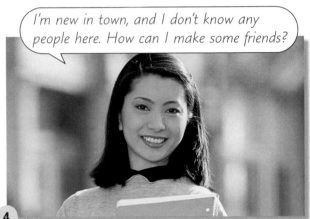

4

It's my best friend's birthday, and I don't have a present for her. All the stores are closed!

5

I have a big test tomorrow. My family is very noisy, and I can't study!

6

A: I can't lose weight. . . .
B: Exercise every day. And . . .

B *Class activity* Think of two problems you have. Then tell the class. Your classmates give advice.

A: I don't understand this activity.
B: Read the instructions again.
C: Don't worry! Ask the teacher.

Student A

A *Pair work* Look at the map. You are on Third Avenue between
Maple and Oak Streets. Ask your partner for directions to these places.
(There are no signs for these places on your map.) Then label the buildings.

garage   supermarket   flower shop

A: Excuse me. How do I get to the garage?
B: Walk down Third Avenue to . . .

B *Pair work* Your partner asks you for directions to three places.
(There are signs for these places on your map.) Use the expressions
in the box to give directions.

Go up/Go down . . .	It's on the corner of . . . Street and . . . Avenue.	It's next to . . .
Walk up/Walk down . . .		It's behind . . .
Turn right/Turn left . . .	It's between . . . and . . .	It's in front of . . .
	It's across from . . .	

Student B

A *Pair work* Look at the map. You are on Third Avenue between Maple and Oak Streets. Your partner asks you for directions to three places. (There are signs for these places on your map.) Use the expressions in the box to give directions.

A: Excuse me. How do I get to the garage?
B: Walk down Third Avenue to . . .

Go up/Go down . . .	It's on the corner of . . . Street	It's next to . . .
Walk up/Walk down . . .	and . . . Avenue.	It's behind . . .
Turn right/Turn left . . .	It's between . . . and . . .	It's in front of . . .
	It's across from . . .	

B *Pair work* Ask your partner for directions to these places.
(There are no signs for these places on your map.) Then label the buildings.

coffee shop   shoe store   bookstore

PAST AND PRESENT

A *Pair work* Ask your partner questions about his or her past and present. Check (✓) the answers.

A: Did you clean your room as a child?
B: Yes, I did. OR No, I didn't.

A: Do you clean your room now?
B: Yes, I do. OR No, I don't.

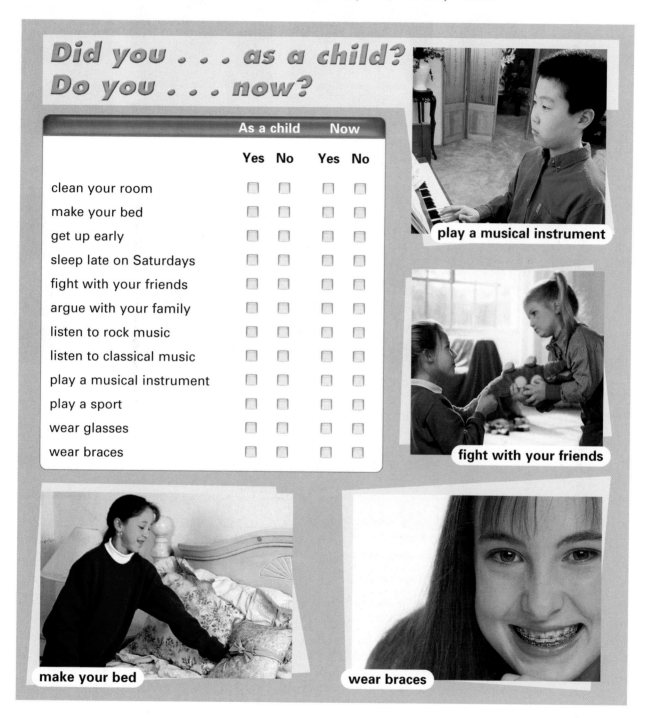

Did you . . . as a child?
Do you . . . now?

	As a child		Now	
	Yes	No	Yes	No
clean your room	☐	☐	☐	☐
make your bed	☐	☐	☐	☐
get up early	☐	☐	☐	☐
sleep late on Saturdays	☐	☐	☐	☐
fight with your friends	☐	☐	☐	☐
argue with your family	☐	☐	☐	☐
listen to rock music	☐	☐	☐	☐
listen to classical music	☐	☐	☐	☐
play a musical instrument	☐	☐	☐	☐
play a sport	☐	☐	☐	☐
wear glasses	☐	☐	☐	☐
wear braces	☐	☐	☐	☐

play a musical instrument

fight with your friends

make your bed

wear braces

B *Group work* Join another pair. Tell them about changes in your partner's life.

"Paulo didn't clean his room as a child, but he cleans his room now."

A What were five important events in your life? Mark the years and events on the time line. Then write a sentence about each one.

I was born . . .

I got a bicycle . . .

I started elementary school . . .

I graduated from high school . . .

I moved to a new place . . .

I won a prize . . .

I fell in love . . .

I got married . . .

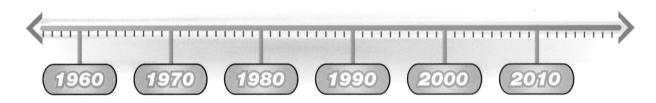

1. *I was born in 1984.*
2. ....
3. ....
4. ....
5. ....

B *Pair work* Ask your partner about his or her time line.

A: What happened in 2003?
B: I fell in love.
A: How old were you?
B: I was twenty-three.

LET'S MAKE A DATE!

A Imagine this is next month's calendar. Write ten plans on the calendar. Use these expressions and your own ideas.

go to (the movies/a party)   play (tennis/basketball)
go (dancing/shopping)   meet (my friend/teacher)
go on vacation   have dinner with (my brother/parents)
study for (a test/an exam)   visit (my parents/grandparents)
go out with (my girlfriend/boyfriend) see (the dentist/doctor)

SUNDAY	MONDAY	TUESDAY	WEDNESDAY	THURSDAY	FRIDAY	SATURDAY
1	2	3	4	5	6	7
8	9	10	11	12	13	14
15	16	17	18	19	20	21
22	23	24	25	26	27	28
29	30	31				

B *Group work* Look at your calendars. Agree on a date to do something together.

A: Do you want to do something on March third?
B: I'd like to, but I can't. I'm going to play volleyball. How about March fourth?
C: March fourth? Sorry, I have to . . .

C *Group work* Make a plan to do something together. Then share your plans with the class.

A: We can all do something on March seventh. Would you like to play tennis?
B: No, I don't play tennis very well. Do you want to go to a museum?
C: Well, I really don't like museums. . . .

Interchange 16

Units 1–16 Self-study

1 PERSONAL INFORMATION

A ▶ Listen to the conversations. Check (✓) the correct names.

1. ☐ Kathy Conner
   ☑ Cathy Conner
   ☐ Cathy Connor

2. ☐ John Wood
   ☐ John Woods
   ☐ Jon Wood

3. ☐ Steven Allen
   ☐ Stephen Allen
   ☐ Steven Allan

4. ☐ Ms. Lewis
   ☐ Mrs. Louis
   ☐ Ms. Louis

B ▶ Listen again. Correct the phone numbers.

1. (6̶5̶6) 555-8890
   4

2. (212) 555-9113

3. (618) 555-1037

4. (319) 555-4037

2 WHERE ARE MY THINGS?

A ▶ Listen to the conversation. Check (✓) the things the people talk about.

B ▶ Listen again. Where are the things? Complete the sentences.

1. The ....*sunglasses are*........ on the table.
2. The .... next to the table.
3. The .... on the chair.
4. The .... under the table.
5. The .... in the purse.

3 WHO'S THAT?

A ▶ Listen to Helen describe her friends. Number the pictures from 1 to 4.

☐

Age: ....
Country: ....

☐

Age: ....
Country: ....

☐

Age: ....
Country: ....

1

Age: ..19..
Country: ..Japan..

B ▶ Listen again. Write the ages and countries of Helen's friends.

4 FASHION SHOW

A ▶ Listen to the fashion show. Check (✓) the things each person is wearing.

	dress	heels	sandals	shirt	shorts	skirt	suit	sweater	T-shirt
1. Kyle	☐	☐	✓	☐	✓	☐	☐	☐	✓
2. Nicki	☐	☐	☐	☐	☐	☐	☐	☐	☐
3. Josh	☐	☐	☐	☐	☐	☐	☐	☐	☐
4. Tina	☐	☐	☐	☐	☐	☐	☐	☐	☐

B ▶ Listen again. Write the colors of each person's things.

1. Kyle *yellow, dark green, light brown*
2. Nicki ....
3. Josh ....
4. Tina ....

5 AROUND THE WORLD

A ▶ Listen to the television show. Write the correct times for each city.

	Time	What are they doing?
1. Natalie (Moscow)	4:00 P.M.	working
2. Ross (Sydney)	....	....
3. Maria (Los Angeles)	....	....
4. Lucy (Paris)	....	....

B ▶ Listen again. What are the people doing? Complete the chart.

6 YOUR WEEKLY ROUTINE

▶ Listen to the questions. Check (✓) the best answers.

1. ☐ It's downtown.	✓ Yes, I do.	☐ In the suburbs.
2. ☐ At 7 A.M.	☐ On weekends.	☐ In the morning.
3. ☐ In the city.	☐ I take the bus.	☐ Every weekday.
4. ☐ I walk.	☐ No, I don't.	☐ Early.
5. ☐ Yes, I do.	☐ At noon.	☐ Every day.
6. ☐ No, I don't.	☐ At 7:00.	☐ Late.
7. ☐ All day.	☐ At home.	☐ In the evening.
8. ☐ On Saturdays.	☐ At 8 P.M.	☐ Yes, I do.

7 KATHY'S APARTMENT

A ▶ Listen to the conversation. What does Kathy like about her apartment? Check (✓) the best answer.

☐ The apartment is big.   ☐ There is a good view.   ☐ She has nice furniture.

B ▶ Listen again. Cross out the things Kathy doesn't have.

bathroom	books	coffee table	kitchen	sofa
bedroom	bookshelves	~~dining room~~	living room	windows

8 MY NEW JOB

A ▶ Listen to the conversation. Check (✓) the correct picture of Bob.

☐   ☐   ☐

B ▶ Listen again. Answer the questions.

1. Where does Bob work?   ....
2. What days does he work?   ....
3. When does he start work?   ....
4. When does he finish work? ....
5. What does he do after work? ....

PARTY MENU

A ▶ Listen to Sue and Fred talk about foods for a party.
Number the foods from 1 to 8.

☐   ☐   ☐   ☐

☐   ☐ 1   ☐   ☐

B ▶ Listen again. Cross out the foods Sue and Fred don't get.

cake	crackers and cheese	~~hamburgers~~	soda
cookies	fruit	potato chips	vegetables

10 SPORTS AND ACTIVITIES

A ▶ Listen to the conversations. Number the pictures from 1 to 4.

☐   1   ☐   ☐

B ▶ Listen again. Check (✓) the questions you hear.

1. ☐ What sports do you play?   3. ☐ When do you practice?
   ☐ What sports do you watch?   ☐ Who do you practice with?

2. ☐ What time do you practice?   4. ☐ Where do you play?
   ☐ How often do you practice?   ☐ When do you play?

11 A BUSY SUMMER

A ▶ Listen to Jill and Kenny's conversation. Write the dates for each event.

Event	Date	What are they going to do?
John's graduation	*June 15th*	*have a party*
Amy and Jeff's wedding		
Parents' anniversary		
Kenny's birthday		

B ▶ Listen again. How are they going to celebrate each event? Complete the chart.

12 HEALTH TALK

A ▶ Listen. What is a different way to say each sentence or question? Number these sentences or questions from 1 to 6.

.... Go to bed early.   .... I have a stomachache.   .... I don't feel well.
..*1*.. How do you feel?   .... My eyes are sore.   .... What's wrong?

B ▶ Listen again. Check (✓) the best response.

1. ☑ I'm just fine, thanks.   3. ☐ I feel better.   5. ☐ That's good advice.
   ☐ What's wrong?   ☐ I have a cold.   ☐ I don't think so.

2. ☐ That's good.   4. ☐ Take some antacid.   6. ☐ I'm sorry to hear that.
   ☐ Maybe I can help.   ☐ Buy some aspirin.   ☐ Try some cough drops.

13 WHERE IS IT?

A ▶ Listen. Where do the people want to go? Number the pictures from 1 to 4.

B ▶ Listen again. Where are the places? Correct the mistakes.

1. It's on Center Street, ~~across from~~ *between* the drugstore and the gas station.

2. It's on Main Street, next to the department store.

3. It's on the corner of Center Avenue and First Street, across from the hotel.

4. It's on the corner of Center Avenue and Fourth Street, across from the drugstore.

14 LAST WEEKEND

A ▶ Listen to the conversations. Did Gary, Debra, and Brian have good weekends? Check (✓) Yes or No.

Gary ☐ Yes ☐ No   Debra ☐ Yes ☐ No   Brian ☐ Yes ☐ No

B ▶ Listen again. Put each person's activities in time order from 1 to 4.

Gary	**Debra**	**Brian** . . . .
.... had a party	.... did laundry	.... met friends
.... cooked food	.... shopped for groceries	.... played volleyball
..1.. played basketball	.... studied for a test	.... went swimming
.... watched a movie	.... cleaned the house	.... had a picnic

15 TIME LINE

A ▶ Listen to an interview with an actress. Write the years you hear on the time line.

1983

B ▶ Listen again. Complete the sentences with the correct years.

1. The actress was born in ...1983... .
2. She graduated from high school in ....
3. She got her first acting job in ....
4. She moved to the U.S. in ....
5. She started acting in ....
6. She was in her first movie in ....

16 HI, KATE!

▶ Listen. There are three mistakes in each message. Correct the mistakes.

1. Hi, Kate! This is Don. My ~~brother~~ *sister* is visiting me, and we're going to see a movie tomorrow night. Do you want to come? Please call me by 5:00 today.

2. Hi, Kate. This is Bill. Sorry I missed your call. I was in the yard. I'd love to have lunch with you tomorrow, but I can't. I have to study for a test. Sorry!

3. Hi, Kate. This is Howard. I was in Mexico last week, so I missed our math class. What did we study? Please call me at home. The number is 555-4509. Thanks.

Self-study audio scripts

1 Personal information

A Listen to the conversations. Check the correct names.

1. MAN: What's your name, please?
    WOMAN: I'm Cathy Conner.
    MAN: Is that C-A-T-H-Y?
    WOMAN: Yes, that's right.
    MAN: And how do you spell your last name?
    WOMAN: It's C-O-N-N-E-R.
    MAN: And what's your phone number, please?
    WOMAN: It's (646) 555-8890.
    MAN: I'm sorry. What's your phone number again?
    WOMAN: (646) 555-8890.
    MAN: Thank you.

2. WOMAN: Are you Jon Woods?
    MAN: No, I'm Jon Wood. W-O-O-D.
    WOMAN: OK, Mr. Wood. And how do you spell your first name?
    MAN: It's J-O-N.
    WOMAN: OK. Now, what's your phone number, please?
    MAN: It's (212) 555-9913.
    WOMAN: Is that (212) 555-9113?
    MAN: No, 9913.
    WOMAN: 9913. Thank you.

3. WOMAN: Hi. What's your name, please?
    MAN: It's Steven Allan.
    WOMAN: How do you spell your first name?
    MAN: It's S-T-E-V-E-N.
    WOMAN: OK. And your last name?
    MAN: It's A-L-L-A-N.
    WOMAN: Great. And your phone number, please?
    MAN: It's (718) 555-1037.
    WOMAN: Is that (718) 555-1037?
    MAN: Yes, that's right.

4. MAN: Is your name Mrs. Lewis?
    WOMAN: No, actually, it's Ms. Lewis.
    MAN: I'm sorry. Ms. Lewis. Now, how do you spell your name? Is that L-O-U-I-S?
    WOMAN: No. It's L-E-W-I-S.
    MAN: OK. And what's your phone number, please?
    WOMAN: It's (319) 555-4073.
    MAN: (319) 555-4703?
    WOMAN: No, 4073.
    MAN: 4073. OK.

B Listen again. Correct the phone numbers.

2 Where are my things?

A Listen to the conversation. Check the things the people talk about.

WOMAN: Oh, no!
MAN: It's OK. Let me help you.
WOMAN: Oh, thank you.
MAN: OK. Uh, . . . here are your sunglasses, on the table.
WOMAN: Thanks. Um, now where's my cell phone?

MAN: Is this your cell phone, next to the table?
WOMAN: Yes. Thanks. Oh, look. Here are my keys, on the chair.
MAN: And, hey, what's this, under the table?
WOMAN: Oh, it's my address book. Uh-oh. Where's my wallet? Is it behind the chair?
MAN: Uh, no.
WOMAN: Oh, wait a minute. Here it is. It's in my purse!
MAN: Is that it?
WOMAN: I think so. Thanks for your help.

B Listen again. Where are the things? Complete the sentences.

3 Who's that?

A Listen to Helen describe her friends. Number the pictures from 1 to 4.

1. MAN: Who's that?
    HELEN: Oh, that's my friend Maiko.
    MAN: She's very pretty. Is she from China?
    HELEN: No, she's not. She's from Japan.
    MAN: How old is she?
    HELEN: She's 18 – no, 19 years old.

2. MAN: Who's he? He looks very serious.
    HELEN: That's my friend David. He's 16.
    MAN: Where's he from? Is he American?
    HELEN: No, he's not. He's Australian.
    MAN: Where in Australia? Sydney?

3. MAN: And who's that?
    HELEN: That's Carlos. He's from Spain.
    MAN: I see. How old is he?
    HELEN: Um, he's 28.
    MAN: Twenty-eight? He looks young.

4. MAN: And who's that?
    HELEN: Oh, that's Carmen.
    MAN: Where is she from?
    HELEN: Colombia. She's really funny.
    MAN: How old is she?
    HELEN: She's 20. She's great.

B Listen again. Write the ages and countries of Helen's friends.

4 Fashion show

A Listen to the fashion show. Check the things each person is wearing.

1. SAM: Welcome to our fashion show. I'm Sam Carson . . .
    BRENDA: . . . and I'm Brenda Black. [applause and music] Let's look at our first model. Kyle is wearing a yellow T-shirt and dark green shorts.
    SAM: Yes, his T-shirt is yellow and his shorts are dark green. And Kyle is wearing sandals.
    BRENDA: Yes, he is. Light brown sandals. Very nice. [applause]

2. SAM: Here comes our second model, Nicki. She's wearing a skirt and a sweater.

BRENDA: Ah, yes. Her skirt is beige and her sweater is orange. Great spring colors! [*applause*]

3. BRENDA: Now here's Josh. Josh is wearing a purple suit and a red shirt!

SAM: Yes, his suit is purple and his shirt is red. Wow!

4. BRENDA: Our last model today is Tina. Tina is wearing a black dress and high heels.

SAM: Oh, very nice. What color are her shoes?

BRENDA: They're white. Tina's dress is black and her shoes are white.

SAM: Black and white! Very exciting! [*applause*]

B Listen again. Write the colors of each person's things.

5 Around the world

A Listen to the television show. Write the correct times for each city.

1. PAM: [*music*] Hello, and welcome to "Around the World." I'm your host, Pam Dayburn. Today we're calling people around the world. We're asking them, "What time is it and what are you doing?" First, we're calling Natalie in Moscow. [*phone rings*] Hello, Natalie.

NATALIE: Hello, Pam.

PAM: What time is it in Moscow, Natalie?

NATALIE: It's 4 P.M.

PAM: Four o'clock, huh? And what are you doing?

NATALIE: I'm at the office. I'm working.

2. PAM: Next, we're calling Ross in Sydney, Australia. [*phone rings*] Hello, Ross!

ROSS: Hi, Pam.

PAM: Ross, what time is it in Sydney?

ROSS: It's five after eleven.

PAM: 11:05 P.M.?

ROSS: Yes!

PAM: And what are you doing?

ROSS: I'm watching television.

3. PAM: Now, we're talking to Maria in Los Angeles. [*phone rings*] Hi, Maria.

MARIA: Hi, Pam.

PAM: What time is it in Los Angeles?

MARIA: Um, it's 5:10 A.M.

PAM: Ten after five in the morning! Wow, you're up early. What are you doing?

MARIA: I'm studying for a test.

PAM: Oh! Well, good luck on the test!

4. PAM: Last, we're calling Lucy in Paris. [*phone rings*] Hi, Lucy!

LUCY: Hi, Pam.

PAM: What time is it in Paris, Lucy?

LUCY: It's 2:15 P.M.

PAM: A quarter after two, huh? And what are you doing?

LUCY: I'm making lunch. I'm really hungry!

PAM: I see. Well, have a good lunch!

B Listen again. What are the people doing? Complete the chart.

6 Your weekly routine

Listen to the questions. Check the best answers.

1. Do you live with your parents?
2. What time do you get up?
3. When do you go to school?
4. How do you get to school?
5. What time do you have lunch?
6. Do you eat dinner with your family?
7. When do you do your homework?
8. When do you sleep late?

7 Kathy's apartment

A Listen to the conversation. What does Kathy like about her apartment? Check the best answer.

MAN: How's your new apartment, Kathy?

KATHY: Well, it's not very big. I have a small bedroom, a kitchen, and a bathroom. But there's no dining room or living room.

MAN: No dining room or living room? That's too bad. What are the other rooms like?

KATHY: Well, I love my bedroom. It has three windows. On a sunny day, I have a really nice view of the city.

MAN: Do you have a lot of furniture?

KATHY: No, not really. I have a sofa and a small coffee table. They're not great, but they're OK. There's also a television. But there are no bookshelves. I have a lot of books, so I really need bookshelves!

B Listen again. Cross out the things Kathy doesn't have.

8 My new job

A Listen to the conversation. Check the correct picture of Bob.

BOB: Guess what, Jenny? I have a new job.

JENNY: Congratulations, Bob! Where do you work?

BOB: At the French restaurant on Center Street.

JENNY: Oh, I know that place. There's a singer at that restaurant on weekends. . . . So, are you a waiter?

BOB: No, I'm the chef!

JENNY: The chef? Wow! So, when do you work?

BOB: I work on Fridays, Saturdays, and Sundays.

JENNY: Great! What time do you start work?

BOB: I start work at 4 P.M.

JENNY: At four in the afternoon? That's late. Do you work late, too?

BOB: Yes. It's a very busy restaurant. I usually finish at one in the morning.

JENNY: One A.M.? Wow! What do you do after work?

BOB: I go home and sleep! I like my job, but after work I'm always tired!

B Listen again. Answer the questions.

9 Party menu

A Listen to Sue and Fred talk about foods for a party. Number the foods from 1 to 8.

SUE: What do you want for the party? We don't have any food – and the party is tomorrow!
FRED: Hmm. How about hamburgers?
SUE: Oh, I don't want hamburgers. Let's just have snacks.
FRED: Like what?
SUE: How about some crackers and cheese?
FRED: Good idea! I love crackers and cheese! And let's get some potato chips.
SUE: Hmm. I don't really want potato chips. They aren't very good for you. I know! Let's have some vegetables. How about carrots and celery?
FRED: Oh, no. I don't want any carrots and celery. People hardly ever eat vegetables at parties.
SUE: OK, then. No carrots and celery. But let's get some fresh fruit. Everyone likes fruit. Maybe strawberries and mangoes?
FRED: Yeah, I like strawberries and mangoes. . . . And we need dessert. I know! Let's get some cake.
SUE: No, cake is too difficult to eat. Let's get some cookies.
FRED: Oh, OK. Anything else?
SUE: Oh, yeah! Do we need any drinks?
FRED: Yeah, we do. Let's get some soda.
SUE: I think that's it. Now let's make a shopping list.

B Listen again. Cross out the foods Sue and Fred don't get.

10 Sports and activities

A Listen to the conversations. Number the pictures from 1 to 4.

1. WOMAN: Do you play any sports?
   MAN: No, I don't. But I like to watch sports.
   WOMAN: What sports do you watch?
   MAN: Hockey. It's always exciting!

2. WOMAN: Wow! I didn't know you can play the violin.
   MAN: Yes. I can play pretty well.
   WOMAN: How often do you practice?
   MAN: Every day.

3. MAN: I love tennis. I play almost every day.
   WOMAN: When do you practice?
   MAN: I practice at 6:30 A.M.
   WOMAN: Six-thirty in the morning? That's early!

4. MAN: Can you play chess?
   WOMAN: Yes, I can. I'm on the chess team at school.
   MAN: Great. Where do you play?
   WOMAN: We usually play in a classroom.

B Listen again. Check the questions you hear.

11 A busy summer

A Listen to Jill and Kenny's conversation. Write the dates for each event.

JILL: This summer is going to be busy.
KENNY: You're right! John's graduation is on June 15th.
JILL: Yes. And Amy and Jeff's wedding is just a week later. On June 22nd.
KENNY: Are we going to have a party for John's graduation?
JILL: Yes, remember? We're going to have a party for all his friends.
KENNY: Oh, yeah. And what about Amy and Jeff's wedding?
JILL: Oh, yes, on June 22nd. Well, I know we're going to give them a present . . . Then, look here. Our parents' anniversary is the next month.
KENNY: Oh, right. When is it again?
JILL: On July 10th. Don't you remember?
KENNY: Right, right. July 10th. So what are we going to do? Are we going to have a party?
JILL: No, I don't think they want a party. I think they want to go out for dinner in a nice restaurant. And what are we going to celebrate on August 9th?
KENNY: My birthday! August 9th is my birthday!
JILL: So, how are we going to celebrate?
KENNY: Are we going to have a picnic? I want to have a picnic!
JILL: That sounds fun.
KENNY: Yeah! It's going to be a great birthday!

B Listen again. How are they going to celebrate each event? Complete the chart.

12 Health talk

A Listen. What is a different way to say each sentence or question? Number these sentences or questions from 1 to 6.

1. How are you?
2. I feel awful.
3. What's the matter?
4. My stomach hurts.
5. Don't stay up late.
6. I have sore eyes.

B Listen again. Check the best response.

13 Where is it?

A Listen. Where do the people want to go? Number the pictures from 1 to 4.

1. WOMAN: Excuse me, where's the supermarket?
MAN: Oh, um, it's on Center Street.
WOMAN: Is it on the corner of First and Center?
MAN: No. It's on Center Street, between the drugstore and the gas station.

2. WOMAN: Can you help me? I'm looking for the movie theater.
MAN: Oh, sure. It's not far from here, on Main Street.
WOMAN: Where on Main Street?
MAN: Let's see . . . It's across from the department store.

3. MAN: Excuse me. Where's the bus stop?
WOMAN: Um, it's on the corner of Center Avenue and First Street.
MAN: Is it across from the drugstore?
WOMAN: No, no, it's next to the hotel.
MAN: Next to the hotel. Thanks a lot.

4. WOMAN: Excuse me. I think I'm lost. I need the post office.
MAN: The post office? It's on the corner of Center Avenue and First Street. It's across from the drugstore.
WOMAN: Thanks a lot!

B Listen again. Where are the places? Correct the mistakes.

14 Last weekend

A Listen to the conversations. Did Gary, Debra, and Brian have good weekends? Check Yes or No.

WOMAN: Hi, Gary. Did you have a good weekend?
GARY: Yeah, it was great. On Saturday, my friends and I played basketball. Then, in the evening, we watched a movie on television.
WOMAN: That sounds like fun. So what did you do on Sunday?
GARY: Oh, Sunday was my dad's birthday.
WOMAN: Great! Did you have a party?
GARY: Yeah. In the afternoon my mom and I cooked a lot of food. Then we had the party in the evening. We all had a great time.

MAN: Did you have a good weekend, Debra?
DEBRA: Well . . . not really. I did laundry on Saturday morning. Then I shopped for groceries on Saturday afternoon.
MAN: Did you go out Saturday night?
DEBRA: No. I didn't. I studied for a test. And I cleaned the house all day on Sunday.
MAN: Wow! You worked hard over the weekend.

WOMAN: Did you go anywhere this weekend, Brian?
BRIAN: Yes, I did. On Saturday, my girlfriend and I went to the beach.
WOMAN: Oh? Did you have a good time?
BRIAN: Oh, yeah! In the morning, we went swimming. Then we had a picnic on the beach.
WOMAN: Sounds nice.
BRIAN: Then we met some friends and played volleyball. We had a great game!

B Listen again. Put each person's activities in time order from 1 to 4.

15 Time line

A Listen to an interview with an actress. Write the years you hear on the time line.

INTERVIEWER: So, Lana, when were you born?
LANA: I was born in 1983.
INTERVIEWER: Were you born in the U.S.?
LANA: No, actually I was born in China.
INTERVIEWER: Interesting. Did you start acting in China?
LANA: No, I didn't. I started acting here, in the U.S.
INTERVIEWER: Tell me, when did you move here?
LANA: Let's see, I was 7 years old. So I moved here in 1990.
INTERVIEWER: And then when did you start acting?
LANA: In 1994.
INTERVIEWER: Wow, you were pretty young.
LANA: Yes, I was only 11. I actually got my first acting job just two years later. I was only 13.
INTERVIEWER: So you got your first acting job in 1996?
LANA: That's right.
INTERVIEWER: What did you do?
LANA: Oh, I did small roles for television on weekends. I did that until I graduated from high school – in 2001.
INTERVIEWER: And then what did you do?
LANA: Well, for two years I did more small roles for television. And then I got my first movie role in 2003.
INTERVIEWER: Was that exciting?
LANA: Oh, yes. It changed my life. . . .

B Listen again. Complete the sentences with the correct years.

16 Hi, Kate!

Listen. There are three mistakes in each message. Correct the mistakes.

1. [*beep*] Hi, Kate. This is Don. My sister is visiting me, and we're going to see a movie tonight. Do you want to come? Please call me by four o'clock today.

2. [*beep*] Hi, Kate. This is Bill. Sorry I missed your call. I was in the shower. I'd love to have dinner with you tomorrow, but I can't. I have to work late. Sorry!

3. [*beep*] Hi, Kate. This is Howard. I was in the hospital last week, so I missed our English class. What did we study? Please call me at home. The number is 555-4590. Thanks.

Self-study answer key

1
A 1. Cathy Conner   3. Steven Allan
     2. Jon Wood   4. Ms. Lewis
B 1. (646) 555-8890   3. (718) 555-1037
     2. (212) 555-9913   4. (319) 555-4073

2
A Check: sunglasses, cell phone, keys, address book, wallet
B 1. The **sunglasses** are on the table.
     2. The **cell phone is** next to the table.
     3. The **keys are** on the chair.
     4. The **address book is** under the table.
     5. The **wallet is** in the purse.

3
A 3, 4, 2, 1
B 1. 19, Japan
     2. 16, Australia
     3. 28, Spain
     4. 20, Colombia

4
A 1. Kyle: sandals, shorts, T-shirt
     2. Nicki: skirt, sweater
     3. Josh: shirt, suit
     4. Tina: dress, heels
B 1. Kyle: yellow, dark green, light brown
     2. Nicki: beige, orange
     3. Josh: purple, red
     4. Tina: black, white

5
A/B Natalie (Moscow): 4:00 P.M. / working
Ross (Sydney): 11:05 P.M. / watching television
Maria (Los Angeles): 5:10 A.M. / studying for a test
Lucy (Paris): 2:15 P.M. / making lunch

6
1. Yes, I do.   5. At noon.
2. At 7 A.M.   6. No, I don't.
3. Every weekday.   7. In the evening.
4. I walk.   8. On Saturdays.

7
A There is a good view.
B ~~bookshelves~~   ~~dining room~~   ~~living room~~

8
A Check the first picture.
B 1. at a French restaurant
     2. on Fridays, Saturdays, and Sundays
     3. at 4:00 P.M.
     4. at 1:00 A.M.
     5. sleep

9
A Top row: 6, 2, 3, 7; Bottom row: 5, 1, 8, 4
B ~~cake~~   ~~hamburgers~~   ~~potato chips~~   ~~vegetables~~

10
A 2, 1, 4, 3
B 1. What sports do you watch?   3. When do you practice?
     2. How often do you practice?   4. Where do you play?

11
A/B

Event	Date	What are they going to do?
John's graduation	June 15th	have a party
Amy and Jeff's wedding	June 22nd	give them a present
Parents' anniversary	July 10th	go out for dinner
Kenny's birthday	August 9th	have a picnic

12
A 1. How do you feel?   **B** 1. I'm just fine, thanks.
     2. I don't feel well.   2. Maybe I can help.
     3. What's wrong?   3. I have a cold.
     4. I have a stomachache.   4. Take some antacid.
     5. Go to bed early.   5. That's good advice.
     6. My eyes are sore.   6. I'm sorry to hear that.

13
A 2, 3, 4, 1
B 1. ~~across from~~   between
     2. ~~next to~~   across from
     3. ~~across from~~   next to
     4. ~~Fourth~~   First

14
A Gary: Yes   Debra: No   Brian: Yes
B Gary: 4, 3, 1, 2   Debra: 1, 2, 3, 4   Brian: 3, 4, 1, 2

15
A 1983, 1990, 1994, 1996, 2001, 2003
B 1. 1983   3. 1996   5. 1994
     2. 2001   4. 1990   6. 2003

16
1. ~~brother~~   sister
   ~~tomorrow night~~   tonight
   ~~5:00~~   4:00
2. ~~yard~~   shower
   ~~lunch~~   dinner
   ~~study for a test~~   work late
3. ~~Mexico~~   the hospital
   ~~English~~   math
   ~~555-4509~~   555-4590

Appendix

Countries, nationalities, and languages

This is a partial list of countries, nationalities, and languages.

Countries	Nationalities	Countries	Nationalities	Countries	Nationalities
Argentina	Argentine	Haiti	Haitian	Peru	Peruvian
Australia	Australian	Honduras	Honduran	the Philippines	Filipino
Austria	Austrian	India	Indian	Poland	Polish
Bolivia	Bolivian	Indonesia	Indonesian	Portugal	Portuguese
Brazil	Brazilian	Ireland	Irish	Puerto Rico	Puerto Rican
Cambodia	Cambodian	Israel	Israeli	Russia	Russian
Canada	Canadian	Italy	Italian	Saudi Arabia	Saudi Arabian
Chile	Chilean	Japan	Japanese	Singapore	Singaporean
China	Chinese	Jordan	Jordanian	Somalia	Somalian
Colombia	Colombian	Korea	Korean	South Africa	South African
Costa Rica	Costa Rican	Laos	Laotian	Spain	Spanish
Cuba	Cuban	Lebanon	Lebanese	Sudan	Sudanese
the Dominican Republic	Dominican	Malaysia	Malaysian	Sweden	Swedish
Ecuador	Ecuadorian	Mexico	Mexican	Switzerland	Swiss
Egypt	Egyptian	Morocco	Moroccan	Tanzania	Tanzanian
El Salvador	El Salvadoran	Nepal	Nepalese	Thailand	Thai
England	English	the Netherlands	Dutch	Turkey	Turkish
France	French	New Zealand	New Zealander	the United Kingdom (the U.K.)	British
Germany	German	Nicaragua	Nicaraguan	the United States (the U.S.)	American
Ghana	Ghanian	Nigeria	Nigerian	Uruguay	Uruguayan
Greece	Greek	Panama	Panamanian	Venezuela	Venezuelan
Guatemala	Guatemalan	Paraguay	Paraguayan	Vietnam	Vietnamese

Languages

Afrikaans	English	Hebrew	Japanese	Portuguese	Swedish
Arabic	French	Hindi	Korean	Russian	Thai
Chinese	German	Indonesian	Malay	Spanish	Turkish
Dutch	Greek	Italian	Polish	Swahili	Vietnamese

Irregular verbs

Present	Past	Present	Past	Present	Past
(be) am/is, are	was, were	have	had	sing	sang
become	became	know	knew	sit	sat
buy	bought	leave	left	sleep	slept
come	came	make	made	speak	spoke
do	did	meet	met	swim	swam
drink	drank	pay	paid	take	took
drive	drove	read	read /rɛd/	teach	taught
eat	ate	ride	rode	think	thought
feel	felt	run	ran	wear	wore
get	got	say	said /sɛd/	write	wrote
give	gave	see	saw		
go	went	sell	sold		

Acknowledgments

Illustrations

Rob De Bank 43
Daisy de Puthod 46 (*top*)
Tim Foley 12, 36 (*top*), 74 (*bottom*), 92 (*top*), SS2, SS10, SS13
Travis Foster 41, SS8
Jeff Grunewald 56, IA11, IA13
Randy Jones *v*, 9, 11, 13, 14, 15, 21, 22, 24, 29, 32, 33, 34, 39, 42, 50, 51, 61, 66, 67, 72, 74 (*top*), 79 (*bottom*), 80, 81, 95 (*top*), 100, 103, IA2, IA5, IA8, IA10

Wally Neibart 88, IA7
Ben Shannon 4, 7, 19, 26, 27, 35, 36 (*bottom*), 37, 52, 53, 59, 75, 79 (*top*), 82, 87, 96, 102, SS3
Dan Vasconcellos 30, 85, 94, 95 (*bottom*), IA6
Sam Whitehead 2, 3, 5, 6, 16, 23, 25, 44, 45, 46 (*bottom*), 47, 64, 89, 92 (*bottom*), 99, 106, 108, IA1, IA4

Photo credits

8 (*Exercise 1*) (*all*) © George Kerrigan/Digital Eyes; (*Exercise 2*) (*all*) © John Bessler
9 (*top row*) © John Bessler; (*bottom row, left to right*) © John Bessler; © Photos.com; © Steven Ogilvy; © Photos.com
10 (*Exercise 5*) (*CD player*) © Photos.com; (*cell phone*) © Masterfile; (*all others*) © John Bessler; (*Exercise 6*) (*umbrella*) © John Bessler; (*chopsticks*) © Steven Ogilvy
12 (*top row, left to right*) © John Bessler; © Alamy; © Steven Ogilvy; (*bottom row, left to right*) © Steven Ogilvy; © John Bessler; © Masterfile
17 (*top to bottom*) © Marcus Brooke/Getty Images; © Joe Cornish/Getty Images; © Yoshio Tomii/SuperStock
18 (*left to right*) © Michael Schmelling/AP/Wide World Photos; © Laura Farr/ZUMA/Corbis; © Chris Martinez/AP/Wide World Photo; © Reuters; © Kunz/AP/Wide World Photos
20 (*top to bottom*) © Adamsmith/Getty Images; © Ty Allison/Getty Images; © Color Day Production/Getty Images
25 (*clockwise from top left*) © Jeff Greenberg/The Image Works; © Alan Eliot Lowinger; © Igor Zotin/NewsCom; © Corbis
32 © Dex Images/Corbis
38 © Nicolas Russell/Getty Images
40 (*top*) © Alamy; (*bottom*) © Laurence Dutton/Getty Images
41 (*left to right*) © Sotographs/Getty Images; © VCG/Getty Images; © Ken Chernus/Getty Images
45 (*left to right*) © Len Grant Photography/Alamy; © Corbis; © Erika Stone; © Karen T. Borchers/San Jose Mercury News/NewsCom
48 (*clockwise from top left*) © Garry Black/Masterfile; © Elizabeth Whiting & Associates/Corbis; © Yiorgos Nikiteas/Eye Ubiquitous/Corbis; © Wojtak Buss/age Fotostock
49 (*left*) © Bryce Harper; (*right*) © Sylvain Grandadam/Getty Images
51 (*left to right*) © Owen Franken/Getty Images; © Reza Estakhrian/Getty Images; © Francisco Cruz/SuperStock; © Getty Images
53 (*left to right*) © Stewart Cohen/Getty Images; © Getty Images; © Corbis; © David Frazier/Getty Images
54 (*top to bottom*) © Duomo/Corbis; © Karl Kuntz/The Image Works; © Getty Images; © Steven Ogilvy
55 (*clockwise from top left*) © Cleve Bryant/Photo Edit; © Tim Boyd/AP/Wide World Photos; © Ed Bock/Corbis; © Masterfile

57 (*left to right*) © Getty Images; © Frank Herholdt/Getty Images; © Thinkstock; © Guy Cali/Alamy
59 (*apples*) © Photos.com; (*all others*) © Steven Ogilvy
60 (*left to right*) © Steven Ogilvy; © Steven Ogilvy; © George Kerrigan/Digital Eyes
61 © Patty Eckersley/Getty Images
62 © Jose Luis Pelaez/Corbis
63 (*mochi*) © George Kerrigan/Digital Eyes; (*all others*) © Steven Ogilvy
65 (*top*) © Getty Images; (*bottom*) © DiMaggio/Kalish/Corbis
66 © Amwell/Getty Images
69 (*clockwise from top left*) © AP/Wide World Photos; © Bob Martin/Getty Images; © Paul A. Souders/Corbis; © Paul H. Nilson/Imperial Valley Press/AP/Wide World Photos
71 (*left to right*) © Alamy; © age Fotostock; © Larry Williams/Corbis; © Getty Images
73 (*top row, left to right*) © Michael Keller/Index Stock Imagery; © Giantstep/Photonica; © Jim Cummins/Getty Images; © Alistair Berg/Getty Images; (*bottom row, left to right*) © Ariel Skelley/Corbis; © Jose Luis Pelaez/Corbis; © GDT/Getty Images; © Jason Dewey/Getty Images
76 (*left to right*) © Nik Wheeler/Corbis; © Peter Sanders/HAGA/AP/Wide World Photos; © Eriko Sugita/Reuters/Corbis
77 (*clockwise from top left*) © Roderick Chen/SuperStock; © Bill Walsh/SuperStock; © Harvey Lloyd/SuperStock; © Paul Barton/Corbis
78 © Steven Ogilvy
80 (*all photos*) © Steven Ogilvy
83 (*number 2*) © Sean Justice/Getty Images; (*number 3*) © Chris Rogers/Corbis; (*number 5*) © David Stoecklein/Corbis; (*number 6*) © Michael A. Keller Studio/Corbis; (*number 7*) © Roy Morsch/Corbis; (*number 8*) © Michael A. Keller Studio/Corbis
86 (*top, left to right*) © David Young Wolff/Photo Edit; © Jose Luis Pelaez, Inc./Corbis; (*middle row, left to right*) © Peter Hvizdak/The Image Works; © SuperStock; © Elie Bernager/Getty Images; (*bottom row, left to right*) © Tony Freeman/Photo Edit; © Robert Brenner/Photo Edit; © Getty Images
89 (*top, left to right*) © Getty Images; © Danny Lehman/Corbis; © Corbis; (*bottom, left to right*) © Getty Images; © John Lamb/Getty Images; © Getty Images
91 (*clockwise from top left*) © Fred George/Getty Images; © Andreas Pollock/Getty

Images; © Dan Lecca/Getty Images; © Thomas A. Kelly/Corbis
93 © Ellen B. Senisi/The Image Works
97 (*left to right*) © John Feingersh/Corbis; © Comstock; © Punchstock
99 © Carlos Alvarez/Getty Images
100 (*left to right*) © Bembaron Jeremy/Corbis Sygma; © Reuters/Corbis; © Eric Robert/Corbis Sygma; © Rufus F. Folkks/Corbis; © Sergio Moraes/Reuters/Corbis
101 © Paul Chesley/Getty Images
102 (*left to right*) © Rufus F. Folkks/Corbis; © Paul Sutton/Duomo/Corbis; © Gregory Pace/Corbis; © Jeff Vespa/WireImage
104 © Corbis
105 © Jim Ruymen/Reuters/Corbis
107 (*top*) © Alamy; (*bottom*) © Larry Williams/Corbis
108 (*top row, left to right*) © Chuck Savage/Corbis; © Tom & Dee Ann McCarthy/Corbis; © Neal Preston/Corbis; (*bottom, left to right*) © David Butow/Corbis Saba; © Ron Watts/Corbis
109 © Lisa Peardon/Getty Images
110 © Mary Kate Denny/Photo Edit
111 (*top row, left to right*) © Hugh Sitton/Getty Images; courtesy of Parrot Jungle Island, FL/www.parrotjungle.com; © Stacey Green/Workbook Stock; (*bottom, left to right*) © AP/Wide World Photos; © Peter Titmuss/Alamy
112 (*left to right*) © Bettmann/Corbis; © Underwood & Underwood/Corbis; © SuperStock
113 © Corbis
IA9 (*all photos*) © Steven Ogilvy
IA12 (*clockwise from top left*) © Gabe Palmer/Corbis; © VCG/Getty Images; © Mark Scott/Getty Images; © Getty Images; © Syracuse Newspapers/The Image Works; © Alamy
IA14 (*left*) © Myrleen Ferguson Cate/Photo Edit; (*right, top to bottom*) © Don Smetzer/Getty Images; © Norbert Schäfer/Corbis; © Michael Newman/Photo Edit
IA15 (*top row, left to right*) Courtesy of Natsu Ifill; © Punchstock; © Ross Whitaker/Getty Images; © Jonathan Nourok/Photo Edit; (*bottom row, left to right*) © Tony Garcia/Getty Images; © Peter Beck/Corbis; © Mike Malyszko/Getty Images; courtesy of Natsu Ifill
SS9 (*top row, left to right*) © Alamy; © Photospin; © Corbis; © age Fotostock; (*bottom row*) (*vegetables*) © Corbis; (*all others*) © George Kerrigan/Digital Eyes